To Bill Fapon fr [illegible]

June 4, 1968

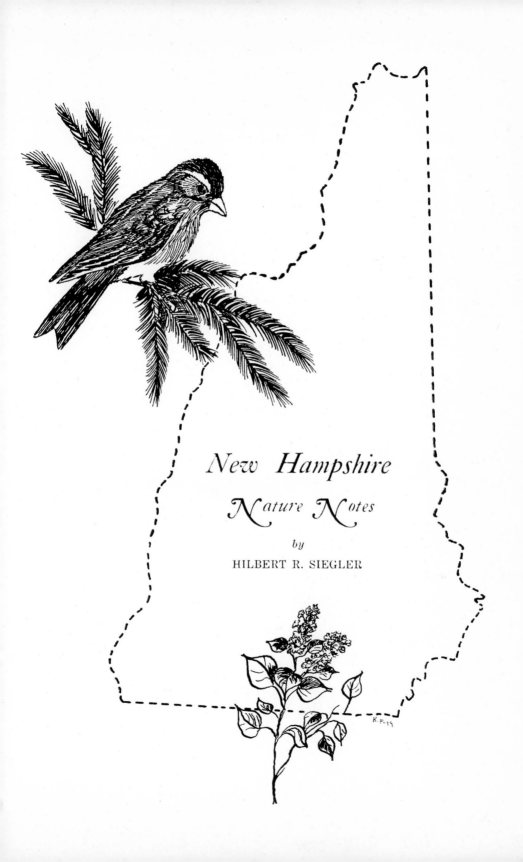

New Hampshire

Nature Notes

by

HILBERT R. SIEGLER

NEW HAMPSHIRE NATURE NOTES

by

Hilbert R. Siegler

Illustrated by

Kenneth T. Fogg, Jr.

PUBLISHED BY

EQUITY

PUBLISHING CORPORATION

ORFORD, NEW HAMPSHIRE

Acknowledgment

The Publisher wishes to acknowledge with appreciation the New Hampshire Fish and Game Department's cooperation in making available the original manuscripts contained in this book, which were prepared by the Department's Chief of Management and Research, Hilbert R. Siegler, for use in its weekly Newsletter. Since the primary purpose for which this material was originally written was to familiarize New Hampshire residents and visitors with the live history and ecology of native species and thus bring about greater sympathy and understanding for professional wildlife management, it is apparent that republication and the additional readership it will attain constitutes an extra dividend for the work invested in the initial project.

Equity Publishing Corporation
Orford, New Hampshire

Dedication

Dedicated to a state that has been good to me. I came to it as a stranger; and New Hampshire gave to me magnificent mountains, extensive forests, clear lakes and rushing streams in abundant profusion, and even a little bit of the Ocean.

The enjoyment of these gifts I now wish to share with others.

H.R.S.

May 1962
Hopkinton, N.H.

Contents

I. BIRDS

BIRDS (Cont.)

II. MAMMALS

MAMMALS (Cont.)

III.   AMPHIBIANS AND REPTILES

IV. FISH

V. INVERTEBRATES

VI. PRINCIPLES AND PHENOMENA OF NATURE

BIRDS

Birds in New Hampshire

People who like to study birds have unusual opportunities to do so in New Hampshire where ornithologists have compiled a list of approximately 330 different kinds. Although this list is small when compared to such champions as Texas where about 550 kinds of birds have been recorded, bird lovers have one unusual advantage in New Hampshire in the fact that a variety of bird groups are found in a small package. Besides the many kinds of birds generally associated with northern forests, strange ocean varieties such as gannets, murres, and dovekies are found from time to time off our coast, Bicknell's thrush on our mountain tops, while the Canada jay, two kinds of three-toed woodpeckers, the crossbills with their X-shaped bills and the spruce grouse in our northern spruce-fir forests, give us a touch of the Arctic. About seventy different kinds of birds brave our winter snows and ice.

The trout fisherman should not think he is the only one eager for the first weeks of May, since New Hampshire bird enthusiasts are no less impatient for this time of year. Little can they be blamed, for into and through our state passes one of the most spectacular migrations of warblers in the United States. About thirty different kinds move through the countryside like a vast army, picking up insects and their larvae by untold millions.

At least sixteen kinds of sparrows have been recorded in New Hampshire, exclusive of the common English sparrow which is not a sparrow but a weaver finch.

Natives may take too much for granted the fact that New Hampshire is a state of thrushes. Nothing so impresses the newcomer to this state as to hear the woods and forests ring with the fluty warbling of veery, wood, and hermit thrushes.

New Hampshire's state bird, the purple finch, can compete with any state bird in the United States in the delicacy of its coloring and its cheerfulness of song.

People who enjoy birds and like to exchange notes can do so in New Hampshire by joining the New Hampshire Audubon Society.

Bird Life in Winter

Many people living in the northern states labor under the impression that, with the exception of a few pigeons, English sparrows, and starlings, bird life in winter is practically nonexistent. They should talk to a group of intrepid souls who annually around Christmas set aside one day to see how many kinds of birds they can find. In New Hampshire, for instance, as many as 66 different species have been recorded along the coast and 42 species inland, all on one winter's day. In some states it reaches a hundred.

The cold weather bird residents can be divided more or less into three main groups. First of all there are those that remain all year round. The ruffed grouse, pheasant and herring gull immediately come to mind. Bluejays, crows, black-capped chickadees, white-breasted nuthatches, and several species of hawks and owls are other examples. Of course, the bluejay around your house in winter is not necessarily the same noisy individual who stayed around your yard during the summer months. The latter might have moved farther south late in fall to be replaced by another.

A second group of winter residents consists mainly of birds seldom found in our states during summer. They bring up their young in extreme northern United States or in Canada and come southward with the snow. Those flocks of tree sparrows, snow buntings, and red polls we find in the drift-covered fields, flitting about like snowflakes in a blizzard, are our winter visitors.

Then there is a sizable group of birds quite erratic in their appearance. Some winters they are so rare that few, if any, are seen. Then there will come a winter when they are seen all over the place. Perhaps no birds demonstrate this idiosyncracy more vividly than do the pine and evening grosbeaks, or the snowy owls. In fact, a student of birds can predict with a fair degree of accuracy what winters one or the other species of these visitors will be common, since their appearances are fairly cyclic. Evening grosbeaks have a two- or three-year cycle, while pine grosbeaks follow a five- to six-year cycle. Snowy owls invade northern United States from the north about every fourth year. There are others, but these serve to illustrate the point.

Of course, there will always be a few crazy, mixed-up robins and even mockingbirds one can find almost any winter. But they just don't fit any kind of a category; they are simply there!

Purple Finch

In the year of our Lord, 1957, on April 25, the purple finch became the state bird of New Hampshire, thus taking a place in prominence alongside the lilac, New Hampshire's state flower. This was fitting, since both have a subdued but attractive coloration of somewhat similar hue. While one makes known its presence through its vivid fragrance, the other does so through its blithesome warbling. It behooves us then to become better acquainted with this new bird of importance.

Purple finches prefer to live in open woods and swamps where firs and cedars are numerous. Often, however, they choose to establish their homes in the vicinity of human houses — especially if ornamental junipers or other conifers are nearby. Their summer range extends from the eastern provinces of Canada southward through eastern United States to northern New Jersey, Pennsylvania and westward to North Dakota. They spend their winter months from southern New England southward to the Gulf Coast.

As do all members of the finch family, purple finches have cone-shaped bills, adapted particularly to eating seeds. Insects are eaten too. Sad to say, these finches also relish the buds of fruit trees. The adult males are attractively colored. Immature males, on the other hand, resemble the drabber appearing females. These finches are from $5\frac{1}{2}$ to $6\frac{1}{4}$ inches in length.

Generally they select the top of trees from which to pour forth their warbling songs. From time to time they launch into the air with vibrating wings, bursting forth with song as they rise ever higher until several hundred feet in the air, when with outstretched wings they descend in wide circles back to the tree from whence they arose. At the height of the breeding season the male will often dance about the female with extended wings, crest erected, and tail spread out, singing softly. The four to six dull greenish-blue eggs spotted with shades of brown, black, and lilac are laid in a frail open-type nest of grass, rootlets and bark strips. The nest is generally lined with hair. These nests are most often found in conifers. No one seems to have taken the time to learn what the incubation period of the eggs is; at least, books do not record it.

7

Loon

The cry of the Common Loon has been described variously as mournful, mirthful, sinister, defiant, uncanny, and demoniacal. This bird is an excellent diver. When underwater in pursuit of fish it often uses its wings, by which means it can at times overtake the swiftest fish. It seldom stays submerged more than a minute, while three to ten minutes is probably a maximum.

While this bird is in its element in water, it becomes a clumsy, wobbling oaf on land. This is mainly due to the fact that its legs are set so far back on its body. It fact, so helpless is the loon on land that it cannot even launch its nine-pound body into the air from there. Even on water it seems to find difficulty getting into the air, often having to flap its wings and run along the water a quarter of a mile. All talk to the contrary, however, it does not need a wind to help it. Once the loon is in the air it is swift and direct in flight. When it decides to alight the loon will spiral down and zoom onto the water like a heavy jet bomber.

The males and females look alike; but loons look different in winter than they do in summer. They have a stout, straight, narrow, and sharp-pointed bill, so constructed that it serves as a spear for catching and holding fish — their main diet. They also feed on crustaceans, mollusks, and other water organisms.

Their nests are very simple structures consisting of a depression in the ground, or made out of some grass, reeds or moss and usually found next to the shore of a lake, on an island, or on top of an abandoned muskrat house from where the incubating bird can make a hurried exit into the water when disturbed. The one to three, but generally two eggs, are olive or brownish with dark spots. Generally laid sometime in May, June and early July, the incubation period is about 29 days. Both sexes incubate. The newly hatched chicks leave the nest within several days, at which time they are often found riding their parents' backs. When 10 to 12 days old they have become proficient swimmers and divers.

Two kinds of loons are found in New Hampshire. Both the Common Loon and the Red-Throated Loon occur along our coast line as migrants and during the winter months; while the former nests throughout the northern two-thirds of the state.

Those wishing to learn more about loons should read *The Common Loon in Minnesota* by Olson and Marshall.

Grebe

Many a duck hunter will remember the time he shot his first "duck" and proudly displaying it before his friends finally discovered it to be a "hell-diver" or grebe. The little pied-billed grebe is perhaps the best known of this group. Six species occur in the United States: red-necked or Holboell's, horned, eared, western, Mexican, and pied-billed; of which three can be seen in New Hampshire, namely the red-necked, horned, and pied-billed grebe. Only the latter nests here, however.

A good place to watch these friendly little water birds during the summer months is Copps Pond in Melvin Village. At times their cuckoo-like and odd whinnying outcries can be heard all over this waterfowl refuge. Grebes put on an active courtship. The male rushes about in an excited manner, splashing along over the surface of the water or diving repeatedly and coming up near the intended mate, voicing his admiration in a variety of cooing notes. They build floating nests in water a foot or more in depth, anchoring them to stems of plants. The nests consist of large masses of plant material piled below the water surface. On top of this and above water a smaller and neater nest is built, measuring about a foot in diameter. The wet, slimy structure is slightly hollowed out to hold the eggs. The three to ten, but usually five to seven, dull white, but often stained brown, eggs are incubated by both sexes. When they leave the nest they often cover the eggs with soft material of the nest.

Incubation takes about 23 to 24 days. The precocious young are able to swim and even dive soon after they hatch. When frightened they will submerge and swim with just the bill showing. Sometimes the parent bird will carry the young on her back.

Grebes feed largely on animal matter such as small fish, snails, frogs, worms, and leeches, and also on parts of aquatic plants.

When these birds are pursued they prefer to escape by diving and hiding but will take off from water to fly when necessary. They seem incapable of rising from the ground.

These grebes breed over most of North and South America. In winter they concentrate mainly along the Southern Atlantic, Gulf and Pacific Coasts, but may be found as far north as the ice-free lakes and rivers.

Wading Birds

One of the most fascinating and interesting groups of birds is that to which belong the herons, bitterns, storks, ibises, spoonbills, and egrets. These are the long-legged wading birds generally found along the muddy flats and shores of lakes and ponds or among the grass and reeds of swamps and marshes. People often mistakenly call them cranes, since both groups have long necks and legs. Cranes, however, always fly with the neck extended, whereas birds of the other group — such as the herons — pull the neck back into the form of an S-curve during flight. Furthermore, while these wading birds have four long, slender toes, without webs, all toes are on the same level whereas the hind toe of the crane is elevated. Ornithologists have placed the various wading birds into three major groups, on the basis of difference in the bill. Spoonbills and ibises have a bill which is grooved along the side from nostril to tip. Storks and wood ibises have a bill which is very thick at the base and is curved near the tip. Herons, bitterns and egrets have a straight, sharp-pointed bill.

The food of all these birds is principally fish, reptiles, amphibians, mollusks, and certain insects, such as grasshoppers.

As a whole, their nests are clumsy, crude affairs. Their young are born naked and helpless.

In North America there are 1 spoonbill and 4 kinds of ibises, 1 wood ibis (which is really stork), 16 different kinds of herons, 3 bitterns and 5 different egrets — but no real storks, despite many white fibs to the contrary. Most of these various waders are found in southern climates — only nine different herons, bitterns and egrets having been reported from New Hampshire.

Herons

One ornithologist writes that the expression "as hungry as a heron" has a basis in fact. As a whole they are gaunt and voracious creatures always half famished and more or less emaciated. To see them silently standing in a marsh, hours at a time in search of food, one would think that fish, frogs, snakes, and other aquatic animals should keep them well supplied with food.

In North America there are 11 different kinds of herons (21 if one takes into consideration the various subspecies), of which 7 have been recorded in New Hampshire. Night Herons, Little Blue Herons, Green Herons, Egrets, and the Great Blue Herons are some of the commoner representatives of this group. A peculiarity of herons is the comb-like process found on the inner side of the claw of the middle toe. While they are generally solitary in their feeding habits, most of them like to congregate in so-called rookeries during the nesting season. The stench and squawking from one nest is sufficient unto itself, but when multiplied it beggars description.

One of the better known herons is the Great Blue Heron. Few birds or other mammals dare to attack this large, formidable bird for it is courageous and armed with a bill that is as powerful and pointed as a spear. A case is on record where an enraged bird struck a wooden oar so forcefully that its bill went through for two inches. A sight to behold is the Blue Heron courtship dance. Groups of these birds gather in a secluded area. The males walk about with an air of great dignity. The birds then form a circle. With outspread wings flapping slowly up and down the herons whirl round and round. Soon one of them jumps into the ring and performs a sort of "heron fling" complete with skips, wing-flappings, and neck curvings. After each act the performer pauses and looks around. His feminine fans croak approval while his male rivals give him the raspberry. Having exhausted his repertory he retires to the ranks to be succeeded by another, until all eligible suitors have put on their act. Of course, from time to time fights ensue. Once the combats are over, the herons leave in pairs. The colony of nests, usually in isolated swamps, is generally in the top of tall trees. New nests made of sticks may be frail, but become larger and bulkier as they are used year after year. From 2 to 7 light blue eggs are laid. The young are fed by regurgitation as the parent stabs downward into their throats. Herons can swim, when forced to.

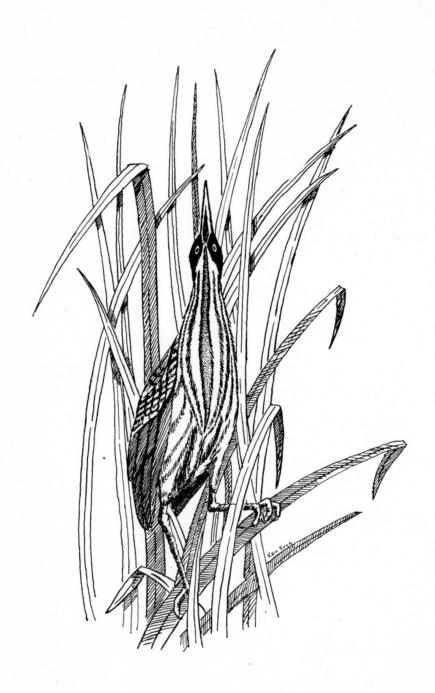

American Bittern

Of all the noises heard in swamps, none is stranger than the "song" of the American Bittern. It resembles the sucking of an old-fashioned wooden pump. And only another bittern could appreciate the gyrations he goes through when he brings forth this song, as the bird suddenly lowers and raises its head and throws it far forward with a convulsive jerk, at the same time opening and shutting the bill with a click, accompanied by a sound which resembles a hiccough. This is repeated a few times, each time a little louder, while the bird seems to be swallowing air. This is succeeded by the pumping noises. Other names given to this bird are Stake Driver or Thunder Pumper, both descriptive of its song, and Marsh Hen or Shipoke.

The bittern's principal food consists of frogs, snakes, mice, crayfish, and other aquatic animals. The bittern is an artist at camouflage and concealment as it stands with its bill cocked up at such an angle that even when in full sight it remains unnoticed because of its close resemblance to a reed or stake. In fact, there are people who swear that they have even seen the bittern sway with the reeds whenever a breeze ripples through.

Whereas most members of the heron family nest in colonies, this species prefers to be alone. The nest, built out of dead rushes, is on the ground among the reeds. The three to seven brownish-gray eggs hatch in about twenty-eight days. The mother feeds the newly hatched young by regurgitation, each youngster in turn seizing the beak of the mother and holding fast until it has gulped its meal. After feeding it flops on its side as though exhausted.

The American Bittern breeds north to a line from British Columbia to Newfoundland and south to a line drawn roughly from southern California through Kansas to North Carolina, and it winters in the southern part of the United States, south to Cuba and Guatemala.

There are in North America two species of so-called bitterns, the American and the diminutive Least Bittern. Both are found in New Hampshire.

Ducks and Geese

With but few exceptions, your chances of seeing a large variety of ducks are better in New Hampshire than in most any northern state in the nation. Of the approximately 42 different species tallied for North America, 29 have been recorded in New Hampshire.

The Atlantic Ocean with its Great Bay in New Hampshire is in large part responsible for this, for off its shores (particularly in winter) can be seen species of ducks which are seldom, if ever, seen inland. Three kinds of Scoters, two of Eiders, and the Old Squaw are typically ocean-dwelling ducks. Here, too, from time to time have been observed rare visitors such as European widgeon and the colorful harlequin duck. The red-breasted merganser, bufflehead, and greater scaup, together with various of our year-round resident ducks, are all common wintering waterfowl in this area. Occasionally one can also see ruddy ducks, canvas-backs, redheads, pintails, gadwalls, baldpates, lesser scaups, and Barrows goldeneyes in New Hampshire, and once in a great while a shoveller may drop by.

New Hampshire is also quite a duck factory. Nesting within our borders are the following ducks, listed in order of abundance: black duck, wood duck, hooded merganser, American merganser, golden-eye, ring-necked duck, mallard, and on very rare occasions, both the green-winged and blue-winged teal.

With exception of an occasional semi-domesticated Canada goose, geese do not nest in New Hampshire in the wild. In fact, bird watchers would do better elsewhere to watch for the 15 different kinds of geese found in North America. Only the Canada goose, snow goose, and brant come over our state during their migrations, and once in a great while a blue goose.

Black Duck

If asked to select a game species which most closely resembled in character a New England Yankee, we would choose the Black Duck. This shy and sagacious bird is the most alert of all ducks. Unlike its close cousin, the company-loving mallard, this independent duck does not generally congregate in immense flocks, but seems to prefer solitude and the company of but a few individuals. Although the Black Duck is found as far west as Minnesota, it is the one species of waterfowl which is concentrated mainly in New England and makes up the greater share of this region's duck population.

Most of the birds hatched and raised in New Hampshire head southward the early part of October. About the time ponds begin to freeze over, there will be another flight of Blacks coming in from the maritime provinces. They will winter at the edge of the ice belt, wherever there is open water, and mainly along the Atlantic Coast. In March these ducks begin their annual trek northward.

New Hampshire is a fairly important Black Duck factory. In late April one can find pairs and small groups on beaver ponds and other waterways throughout the state. While the nuptial flights are in progress one can see two or three ducks flying full speed at tree-top level, as if playing aerial tag.

Nests are built in a large variety of situations: swamps, grassy meadows, and even in woods — generally on the ground. The hollowed-out nest, lined with grass and covered with down, is well concealed with leaves and debris while the eggs are being laid. There may be from 6 to 12, usually 8 to 10, whitish or dull buff-colored eggs, which take from 26 to 28 days to hatch. The female does all the incubating, since the male has deserted her by this time to start his annual moult.

After hatching, the young remain in the nest but a few hours, and then are led away by the mother. Growth and development of flight feathers in the young goes on simultaneously with the moult in the adults, so that both reach the flight stage together in September.

Is there a red-legged variety of Black Duck? Despite considerable controversy relative to the matter, the general belief now is that Blacks gradually become red-legged in their older age and that this is not an indication of two races.

21

Wood Duck

Wood ducks lead a precarious existence, and it is a wonder any are left. Their troubles start before they hatch and generally bring them to an untimely end at a young age. First of all, man has made it increasingly difficult for woodies to find nesting sites. Not only does he destroy many beaver dams whose impoundments create ideal home areas for young ducklings, but he has removed many of the hollow trees in the vicinity of lakes and streams. To offset this piece of mismanagement, sportsmen in New Hampshire have put out duck nesting boxes. In many cases, however, the wood duck's Number 1 enemy, the intelligent raccoon, has discovered what these boxes are for. Not only is he fond of eggs, but he has no compunctions of conscience about destroying the incubating hen if he can catch her on the nest. So prevalent is predation by this mammal that much thought and effort has been devoted toward discouraging it. In New Hampshire, an idea developed by biologists in Massachusetts is currently being utilized, namely, attaching a funnel to the entrance of nest boxes. This funnel permits the duck to enter but eliminates the coon. One difficulty with its use is that fewer ducks use boxes having these attachments. Consequently, we use them only where raccoons are known to be numerous.

Squirrels, minks, some snakes, and other predators also enjoy duck eggs and even the newly hatched duckling. For this reason, perhaps, the mother duck entices her young out of the nest cavity very soon after they hatch — sometimes before all eggs are hatched. At this time those not strong enough to climb to the opening to jump out at their mother's call are eliminated. It is not known if any perish in their exit from the nest, probably depending on where the duckling lands.

Then there is the dangerous march to water which sometimes covers more than a mile and occasionally leads right across major highways. Without a doubt, predation during the trip is high and here again some of the weak probably perish along the way. At Burlington, Iowa, the late Aldo Leopold noted a loss of 61 ducklings from 189 he observed starting the journey from nest boxes to the Mississippi River, at the bottom of a steep bluff and about a city block away. Once in the water these little fluffs of down become particularly appealing to snapping turtles, pickerel, bass, weasels, hawks, owls, foxes, raccoons, and even dogs.

If flight patterns of the past several years were typical, we can assume that wood ducks start leaving New Hampshire early in September, that the greatest exodus takes place the last week in September and the first week in October, and that there are still a goodly number left in the state on opening day of the hunting season, the second or third weekend in October — particularly in southern New Hampshire. This emigration of woodies receives top priority by the New Hampshire Fish and Game Department when consideration is given to establishment of the annual duck hunting season. Two goals are kept in mind: first, the continued preservation of our native stock and, second, an opportunity to harvest a reasonable number by New Hampshire's duck hunters.

We have seen how precarious is the existence of the woodie. Only a fraction survive the period from egg to adulthood and even then predation continues to take its toll. As adults, man becomes their greatest predator. Studies by our biologists, as well as those of technicians of other states, have shown fairly conclusively that wood ducks have a strong homing instinct. Some which have been banded in nesting boxes one year have been found in the same box the following year. Many adults and their offspring will return to the same pond year after year. For this reason woodies are more susceptible to gunning than many other duck species. Once the hunter locates a favorite site he can, if persistent, eradicate an entire family. This often results in a pond without wood ducks for years to come, unless a curious newcomer discovers the area.

Since New Hampshire with its hundreds of pot holes, beaver ponds, and river cut-offs acts as an important wood duck factory, we believe we should also be privileged to harvest a reasonable number. Therefore, the opening of the hunting season is set early enough to get at least a fraction of woodies before they head down the Atlantic Coast. But we also want to maintain a good breeding population of this beautiful bird, so the season is set just late enough to miss the peak of the exodus.

Admittedly there is a great toll of them as they move past many thousands of hunters before reaching their wintering grounds, but the chance that an entire family is eradicated is considerably less than it would have been had the sportsmen gunned for a particular flock on its home pond.

Canada Goose

Among the earliest water birds to sense the restlessness of Spring is the Canada Goose, and by March the V-shaped or single lines of honkers can be observed winging northward to their nesting grounds. Led by experienced old ganders the flocks, flying by night or day, stopping to rest or feed only when necessary, arrive on their breeding grounds soon after the ice is out. While most of the Canada Geese nest in the provinces, a sprinkling of them may be found south of the Canadian border, and quite a few in the western states. In the meantime, the one-year old youngsters may loiter along the way well into the summer, since they do not nest their first year of life.

These geese mate for life. Preliminary to such pairing off they go through interesting courtships. Once the mating has been accomplished, the serious business of nesting begins. Most nests are built on the ground, although occasional individuals have been known to occupy the nests of ospreys or hawks in trees. Nests, made of grass, reeds or leaves, and lined with down, may be in depressions but more often on mounds. Muskrat houses are favorite sites.

Incubation of the 6 to 7 white eggs takes from 28 to 30 days and is performed entirely by the goose, while the gander stays near by as staunch defender. Soon after the young are hatched, the parents begin their annual moult, and for a time may be flightless. These geese are extremely wary, and are keen of sight and hearing. When a flock is out feeding, they will inevitably have one or more sentinels constantly on guard watching for danger.

Whereas the Canada Goose is seldom recorded as nesting in New Hampshire, flocks of these birds always make it a point to let us know that spring or fall has arrived when they pass over our state on their way to and from their nesting grounds. Some even stop over to rest on our many lakes. In fact many hundred to several thousand like New Hampshire well enough to stay through the winter months on Great Bay.

Hawks

Of about 37 different kinds of hawks found in North America, north of Mexico, 15 have been recorded in New Hampshire.

The carrion-eating vultures are represented by an occasional Turkey Vulture during the summer months. The accipiters, or bird hawks, whose short rounded wings and long tail enable them to dart through thickets and woods, have three representatives in our state — an occasional Goshawk, the fairly common Sharp-shinned Hawk, and the uncommon Cooper's Hawk.

Not too many people seem aware of the fact that both the Bald and the Golden Eagle occur in New Hampshire; in fact, both are known to nest in this state. Grouped with the eagles are our large broad-winged buzzard hawks which soar and circle high in the sky. Four different species can be found in New Hampshire: the Red-tailed Hawk, Red-shouldered Hawk, and Broad-winged Hawk nest here, although they are rarely seen here in winter, while the very useful Rough-legged Hawk occasionally migrates into New Hampshire from Canada during the winter months. The harrier group is represented by the Marsh Hawk, commonly seen flying low over open fields; a hawk no one can fail to identify once he sees the white patch on the upper part of the tail near the rump. While these birds are rarely seen here in winter, a certain number nest in our state during the summer.

Then there are the long narrow-winged and tailed falcons. The Peregrine Falcon or Duck Hawk, occasionally found nesting in New Hampshire's cliffs, is one of the swiftest of all birds. It can fly 90 miles per hour and has been clocked doing over 175 miles per hour in a power dive. Another falcon found in our state, of which some may even nest here, is the Pigeon Hawk. The pretty little Sparrow Hawk is, of course, a common sight along telephone wires. It, too, nests here.

Finally, there are the ospreys or fish hawks, of which our lone representative is the American Osprey. Hawks are beneficial to man through their constant attrition on all types of rodents. Like owls, hawks regurgitate the indigestible parts of their food in the form of pellets, making it easy to study their food habits. Today, all hawks are protected in New Hampshire.

Eagles

People often ask how to tell a bald from a golden eagle. It is difficult to differentiate the young birds in flight, since both are uniformly dark colored; however, the young golden eagle has a dark band on the rear margin of a white tail. Identification becomes easy when observed from close-up, since the legs of the golden are feathered to the toes while those of the bald are bare an inch or more above the base of the toes. Eagles mature in three years, and thereafter the bald eagle has a white head (from which it derives its name).

Many ornithologists wonder why the bald eagle was selected as our national emblem rather than the more magnificient golden eagle. The former is apt to be a scavenger, generally found along rivers, lakes and the ocean where it picks up dead fish. On the other hand, the golden eagle is a hunter, once flown only by kings when falconry flourished in Europe. Admittedly, this bird is found in other countries besides North America and perhaps the bald eagle was selected as our emblem since it is found only in North America, ranging from the Arctic southward to northern Mexico.

Despite the fact that the golden eagle is very rare east of the Rocky Mountains, several pair are known to nest in New Hampshire. The bald eagle is more common in our state. Female eagles are larger than the males. Both species have a wingspread of between 6 and 7½ feet, with the golden being somewhat larger. Their courtships consist of spectacular flight maneuvers, circles, and dives, in which both sexes participate. The nests are built in large trees, from 20 to 90 feet above the ground, or on cliffs. Golden eagles are more apt to select high cliffs. Large, coarse sticks, roots, turf and moss make up the nest. The eagles, which mate for life, may use the same nest year after year, generally adding material each spring, so that a golden eagle's nest may eventually be 4 or 5 feet in diameter.

The bald eagle lays from 2 to 3 white eggs, and the golden from 1 to 4 (usually 2) white eggs, marked with purplish spots. Incubation is about 30 to 35 days, the female doing the setting while the male brings her food. The young leave their nest when they are about 9 to 11 weeks old.

Sparrow Hawk

The little Sparrow Hawk is one of the prettiest, tamest, and most sociable of hawks. This grave little falcon is commonly seen perched along telephone lines or hovering with swift-beating wings almost motionless over fields watching for grasshoppers and mice.

This bird is widely distributed throughout all but the Arctic regions of the Western Hemisphere. Although there are twenty-three different subspecies, only the Eastern Sparrow Hawk is found in New Hampshire. It nests from northern Canada south through the United States into the southern states. It shifts somewhat farther south in winter with the northern edge of its range as far north as Kansas and part of New Hampshire.

This is one hawk which nests in tree cavities, crevasses in rocks, holes in banks, on buildings adjacent to houses, and even in bird boxes. As is normal with hawks, the female is larger than the male, and during the mating season in April and May, when both perform aerial gymnastics, she is the aggressor. The three to seven, but usually four or five, whitish eggs are covered with fine brownish spots. Incubation, mainly by the female, takes about twenty-nine or thirty days.

A peculiarity noted about the young in their nest is that the females seem invariably to be more aggressive and ill-dispositioned than the males. Another peculiarity is the fact that this is one of the few instances among birds in which the sexes are unlike in their juvenile plumage.

Although this little hawk subsists mainly on grasshoppers and other insects, it will occasionally take young birds and small rodents. As a whole, however, this hawk is beneficial. Anyone who likes to have pet birds as a hobby will find the dignified male sparrow hawks interesting.

Osprey

There is a hawk that spends a lifetime doing what many of us would like to do. The American Osprey, or fish hawk, devotes practically all of its time to fishing, since it lives almost entirely on fish. For this reason it prefers to live near large bodies of water such as the Atlantic Ocean, large lakes and streams. Ospreys have remarkable eyesight, being able to see fish in water from several hundred feet in the air. When a fish is sighted, the osprey plunges downward with half-closed wings, striking the water breast first with wings extended upward, and seizes the fish in its strong talons. Sometimes the osprey will completely submerge in its plunge. Any kind of fish swimming near the surface will be taken, some weighing as much as four to six pounds. In fact, ospreys have been known to tackle such large fish that they have been dragged under and drowned. Once the fish is captured the osprey rises with it in its talons. The fish is invariably carried head first.

These interesting birds winter in the southern United States and southward, and nest as far north as northern Canada. They return to the northern part of New Hampshire in March and April. It is believed that ospreys mate for life. As soon as they arrive on their breeding grounds they begin to repair their nests, which are used year after year. These large bulky affairs are generally made of sticks, seaweed, and many miscellaneous items, placed up in tree tops, windmills, and other high places. They are often in colonies. Residents along the Atlantic Coast often place a wagon wheel on a pole to attract ospreys. Courtship consists of aerial gymnastics. The two to four whitish eggs with brownish spots take about twenty-eight days to hatch, the female doing the incubating. The young remain in the nest about eight weeks, and then spend most of the summer in the company of their parents learning how to fish.

This is a peaceful hawk. Small birds often build their nests unmolested in the base of the osprey's nest. The bald eagle is this bird's worst enemy, often attacking the osprey to rob it of its fish.

This beautiful and graceful hawk, sometimes having a wingspread of six feet, should receive full protection.

Ruffed Grouse

In 1947 the New York State Conservation Department published a 915-page book entitled *The Ruffed Grouse — Life History — Propagation — Management* by Bump, Darrow, Edminster, and Crissey. This monumental piece of work was based on thirteen years of research by a large technical staff. The book brings together what is known about this grouse; it adds much that the study has brought to light; and it leaves all too many questions still unanswered. This chapter will be devoted to some of the highlights of this book, to some of the new information uncovered in New Hampshire concerning grouse, and to a discussion of hopes and plans for the future.

The ruffed grouse is known by many different names in the United States. In New Hampshire it is known mainly as grouse or partridge. Indians picturesquely referred to it as "carpenter bird" because it pounded on a log. The word "grouse" seems to have been derived from the French terms "greoche", "greiche", and "griais", meaning spotted bird. The term "ruffed" refers to the collar on the bird's neck and not to its disposition.

Its range is greater than that of any other nonmigratory North American game bird, extending from coast to coast across Canada and into Alaska, as well as south into the mountains to central Utah and northern Georgia. In New Hampshire grouse are statewide.

It is now common knowledge that grouse populations go through radical fluctuations. This has evidently been going on for many years. In 1832 Thomas Nuttall, an ornithologist of some renown, wrote that in November, 1831, while travelling nearly to the extremity of New Hampshire, "not a single bird of the species (grouse) was now to be seen". This may come as a shock to some of the old-timers who talk about the good old days. On the other hand, there were also periods when grouse were here in great numbers, probably more than are now seen.

There are two color phases of ruffed grouse in New Hampshire — red or gray ones, irrespective of age or sex. Males usually have longer tail feathers than females. Exact measurements are as follows: for immature grouse, individuals with tails less than 5 3/8" in length are females while those with tails over 5 1/2" are males. Adult grouse having tails less than 5 5/8" in length are females and those with tails longer than 5 3/4" are males.

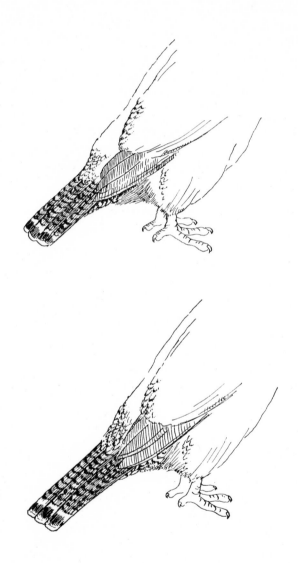

To determine what we don't know about the ruffed grouse, it might help to make a brief inventory of the things we do know.

The average body temperature of grouse is just over 107° F. The adult bird must consume food equivalent to 78 calories to maintain weight during moderate temperatures. The average adult male weighs about 1 ℔. 7 oz. while the female weighs about 1 ℔. 5 oz. When the weight of the former drops below one pound and the latter below 14 ounces, they are in critical condition.

The hunter who shoots a grouse in fall will find the toes of his bird lined with a row of little rods. These grow there in fall and are shed in the following spring. They serve as snowshoes for the winter.

Most everyone living in the country in New Hampshire has had the pleasure of hearing a ruffed grouse drum in spring. Newcomers may have heard it and thought it was the neighbor having a hard time getting his pump motor started. Although drumming can occur any time during the year, it is normally part of a ritual the male performs during the mating season. Many people argue that the grouse makes this noise by beating his wings on a log. It is actually produced by the bird's wings beating against the air.

The activities of mating grouse in spring and early summer normally fall into three phases: strutting, gentle, and fighting. As early as March the males begin to show signs of aggressiveness by strutting about with spread tail and ruff, and as the season progresses, hissing and violent head shaking are added to the strutting performance. Occasionally they may select a high point and drum. At this stage of the game the female seems somewhat bored by it all and tries to keep out of his way. Then there comes a brief period, lasting several days, when the male seems subdued. His whole attitude is the epitome of gentleness, moving about as though in a trance. At this time the female becomes interested in the male and is inclined to lead him about, oftentimes singing. Not long thereafter the male's attitude changes once more. He again begins to strut and gradually, as his interest in the female wanes, he develops a strong fighting mood, ready to take on all comers. This is the period during which the female is laying and incubating her eggs.

The ruffed grouse is New Hampshire's most important game bird; therefore, a discussion of this bird will be continued in more detail than usual.

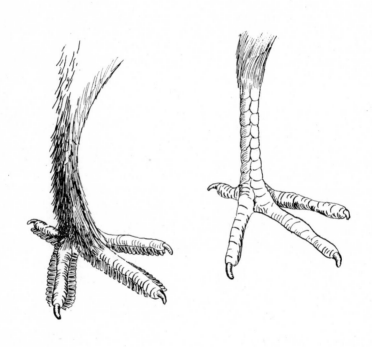

The hen generally lays from nine to fourteen eggs, varying in color from milky white to cinnamon buff. It normally takes 23½ days for the eggs to hatch. Individual females do not rear more than one brood during any one season, but a hen whose first nest is destroyed frequently lays a second clutch.

The chicks leave the nest within a few hours after hatching and will remain as a family unit until about mid-September. The growing grouse go through three general feather phases which can be grouped broadly as natal, juvenile, and adult. When the chick hatches it is covered with down. Juvenile feathers, however, begin to appear immediately after hatching and first become noticeable on the fourth day. Sportsmen may have noticed that grouse several weeks old have feathers which are tipped with down. This happens because the feather which replaces the down develops in the same follicle as the down. As the feather emerges the down is shoved ahead of it, remaining attached to the tip of the new feather.

Flight feathers and those where the wings join the body appear first. When the chick is two weeks old pinfeathers of juvenile plumage are found on all parts of the body. At about three weeks of age the back is covered with feathers. The head region is last to be covered. At about seven weeks of age adult feathers begin to push out the juvenile feathers, just as the latter did the down. The bird is completely covered by adult plumage between eighteen and twenty weeks of age. In spring a slight thinning of feathers occurs all over the body. Most feathers which drop at this time are not replaced until fall.

The person who gives this step by step development of feathers a little thought will be struck by the orderly process of nature in which every proceeding has a purpose and function. The flight feathers which develop first help the chick escape its many enemies. At the same time these growing wing feathers, together with the "shoulder" feathers, form a cover over the chick where it is most vulnerable — the lung region. The back is covered with feathers at about three weeks, when the chick is being weaned from the brooding mother. And the adult grouse would be quite uncomfortable in summer but for the fact that feathers shed in spring are not replaced until fall.

Have you ever shot a grouse weighing two pounds? If you have, your bird was approaching a record. The heaviest bird found during thirteen years of study in New York State weighed 2 pounds 4 ounces.

Since all of New Hampshire's current studies of grouse are for the purpose of maintaining and increasing the present grouse population, it is very important that we know as much as possible about this bird's habits and, particularly, its requirements. For instance, we must know how much territory grouse require in which to live and raise their families. It is known that adult grouse, as a rule, tend to live year in and year out in fairly small areas. This is usually in the vicinity of and including the covert in which they spent their first breeding season, so long as this territory has adequate shelter and satisfactory food at all seasons and in suitable relation to one another. A 25-acre tract of land with good cover may be large enough to support a pair of grouse throughout the year. The poorer the cover the greater the territory needed to maintain these birds. "It is seldom", concluded the New York technicians, "that the territories of individual birds exceed 150 acres or an area, roughly, one-half mile in diameter." There are seasonal shifts within grouse territories. In winter the birds tend to concentrate in the vicinity of conifers, while in the spring they spread out over the second growth hardwood and overgrown brush areas. In the summer there is an increased use of the cut-over areas, while in the fall any portions of their domain offering fruit — such as hawthorn, wild apples, and grapes — are favored.

The fact that grouse live their life in a small territory does not mean they do not move greater distances. Each autumn we read of grouse crashing through windows and in general going through very erratic flights. In fact, it has become known as the "crazy flight". Done mainly by young birds of the year, it might be Nature's way of dispersing them before they settle down. Grouse are capable of covering over a mile without stopping, and can approach speeds of 50 miles an hour, although the average is about 40 miles per hour.

It has generally been assumed that grouse do not migrate. However, studies in Wisconsin, in which large numbers of birds are being banded, may throw new light on the matter.

Let us summarize some of the conclusions reached by the large crew of technicians in New York who devoted thirteen years of study to this game bird.

Food is seldom a problem in grouse management. With the exception of the first two weeks after hatching when the chicks live primarily on insects, grouse subsist mainly on a great variety of

plants — seeds, fruits, leaves, and buds. The maximum number of these food plants is present three to five years after heavy lumbering. Some gravel or grit is needed by the grouse to help it digest its food.

The study brought out that severe cold and heavy snows in January and February have little effect on grouse populations, but severe weather in March does. Findings concerning the effect of inclement weather on newly hatched broods were inconclusive. For this reason New Hampshire is continuing investigations on this specific problem.

Foxes and weasels proved to be the principal predators of nests, Cooper's and Sharp-shinned Hawks among the chicks, while the great horned owls and foxes were the most efficient in preying on adult grouse. In all cases predation varied inversely to the presence and abundance of buffer species such as rabbits and mice.

Inbreeding probably does not occur to any great extent and when it does it exerts no observable detrimental influence.

No evidence was brought to light indicating a relationship between disease and grouse population fluctuations. The most frequent cause of death from disease was due to an inflammation of the stomach caused by a small roundworm parasite. The most common parasite was found to be a large intestinal roundworm which, however, seems to do little harm to grouse. Here in New Hampshire hunters often find an external fly-like parasite on grouse kown as the louse fly. It probably has little effect on them.

One of the most important problems, the effect of hunting on grouse populations, was not solved. Due to the relationship of this factor to grouse management, a number of states are currently investigating it. New Hampshire appears to be in a good position to make a dent in this riddle, since we now have developed a reasonable census method to follow grouse population trends on a state-wide basis.

Spruce Grouse

In a few isolated sections of northern New Hampshire one can still come across a very strange bird — strange because this bird simply refuses to accept the fact that man is not to be trusted. For this reason the Spruce Grouse (called Spruce Partridge, Black Grouse, or Canada Grouse by many people) has been exterminated over much of its range in the United States. The few still to be found are now located in dark spruce forests, tamarack swamps, or mountain tops of our northern wilderness areas. So tame and trusting is this bird that it will sit on a branch and watch a passer-by come within a few feet of it. Full-grown birds have been caught in the hand or beheaded with a switch. A brood in the trail will merely step aside and watch the passer with a sort of affectionate regard.

This grouse somewhat resembles our common ruffed grouse. There are certain decided points of difference, however. The tail is black, broadly tipped with orange-brown. Over the eye is a red-colored patch of naked skin. The whole bird is more slate colored than the reddish or gray-brown of the ruffed grouse. The male is splotched with black beneath, which is lacking on the female.

The mating habits of this bird also differ somewhat from the common grouse. In spring the male spruce grouse struts about with bristling feathers, head, neck and tail raised, and the tail expanded. The drumming is done by beating the air with its wings as it climbs up a leaning tree trunk, or it may fly into the air nearly to the tree tops, or often only a few feet high, and drum suspended with beating wings.

Nests are found on the ground, generally under low conifer branches, in brush heaps, or under tamaracks. These are made of dry twigs and leaves lined with moss and grass. The 8 to 14 eggs are buffy or reddish-brown, blotched with shades of darker brown.

The fact that a few of these tame individuals are still left in New Hampshire should offer an unusual challenge to the sportsmen of New Hampshire — an opportunity to vindicate the thoughtlessness of men in the past by demonstrating that at least one wild creature can trust man and continue to survive. And anyhow, since so much of this bird's diet consists of spruce and fir foliage, its flesh is unpalatable.

Pheasant

The question often arises in New Hampshire as to how long an outsider must live here before he ceases to be a "foreigner". For instance, has the pheasant lived here long enough to be considered a New Hampshirite? In 1793 Governor Wentworth released several pair around Wolfeboro. They disappeared. In 1893 John Gould of Lebanon planted some. By 1912 pheasants were becoming common in the Mt. Vernon and Brookline areas and thereafter they gradually increased in other parts of the state.

The ring-necked pheasants are natives of Asia. The first successful planting of these birds in the United States was made in 1881 in the Willamette Valley of Oregon. These were probably pure Chinese Ringnecks. Since that time other strains such as Mongolian, Japanese, and common English have been introduced so that pure strains are now few and far between. Although attempts have been made to get pheasants started in practically every state of the Union, they have done best in Yankee country north of the southern boundary of Pennsylvania in eastern United States, and in the West north of a line connecting San Francisco and southern Colorado. South Dakota has probably produced the greatest number.

The average male pheasant in fall weighs about 2¾ pounds, while the female averages about 2¼ pounds. Since pheasants do not live long, a large portion (about 70 per cent) of those found in the field each fall will be young of the year. A rapid way of telling a juvenile from an adult male bird is by measuring the length of the spur. On most young the spur will be less than ¾ inch long while it is generally longer than this on adults.

During the fall and winter months pheasants congregate in small flocks composed of either sex, immatures and adults. At that time of the year the males have small bare patches of red skin around the eye. As the mating season approaches these patches of skin gradually become bright red wattles that practically cover the sides of the head.

Male pheasants begin to leave winter concentrations toward the end of February and during March, moving out to establish so-called "crowing territories". These consist of somewhat indefinite areas which the ringneck stakes out and claims as his personal

property to be defended against trespass by other cocks. Hens, however, are always welcome. Boundary disputes often arise between neighboring cocks, resulting in fights. On rare occasions they will battle to the death of one or the other.

Within this territory there may be several places from which the cock crows regularly. While to us this crowing may sound like the last desperate screech before being dunked in the brink, it must be very enticing music to hen pheasants. They gradually drift on to these "crowing territories" and become part of the cock's harem. These harems vary in number, depending on the number of hens available and probably the cock's virility and the vigor of his crowing. Some males have been found to have as many as 18 hens in their harem. One penned cock was known to have taken care of fifty hens. Once the hen has laid her eggs, and the chicks are hatched, however, the male takes no care of the young.

Nesting takes place in April and May, although the actual time may vary several weeks from year to year, depending on weather in spring. Not much effort is taken in making the nest, which is on the ground, generally in hayfields, along fence rows, and in or adjacent to open fields.

The nest will contain an average of 12 to 13 eggs, although this number decreases the later in the spring the eggs are laid. If the nest should be destroyed, the hen may renest. Once the eggs have hatched, however, and the brood destroyed, it is doubtful that the hen will renest. The incubation period is about 23 days. To determine the length of time it took a hen to lay a clutch of eggs, multiply the number of eggs by 1.3.

The hatching chicks are completely covered with down and can leave the nest soon after hatching. By the end of the second week they can make short flights and within 5 or 6 weeks the young are fully feathered. By 8 or 9 weeks adult feathering begins to show up.

Anyone wishing to learn more about pheasants should read *Pheasants in North America* by Durward L. Allen.

Bobwhite Quail

Many an oldtimer still speaks wistfully of days gone by when the Bobwhite Quail was common in New Hampshire. Well they might, for it is difficult to imagine a more cheerful bird, one more useful to the farmer, and one so appealing to the sportsmen with bird dogs. Many an explanation has been advanced to explain the disappearance of the Bobwhite from northern New England. Predators and over-hunting have been given most of the blame. There is, perhaps, a more logical reason. This quail is associated with the small field — weed and grain — adjacent to swampy tangle, thickets, and briar patches. Consequently, when the early settlers spread through the country and opened up the forests, the bobwhite began to increase, following the plow westward and northward. In the early days of rail fences, corn and grain patches, habitat conditions were most ideal for this bird. Today, with New Hampshire again mostly forested and little if any grain left to tide this bird over the winter months, our state has lost its bobwhite habitat. The only coveys to be found are perhaps a few around the fields of bird dog trainers who periodically liberate them.

There are about seventy species of quails and partridges in the western hemisphere; but only seven kinds of quail are found in the United States. The bobwhite is the only representative of this group in eastern United States. It ranges west to eastern Texas (where it blends in with the Mexican bobwhite), eastern Colorado and the Dakotas. Numerous plantings, however, have established colonies farther west of this range.

As is well known, bobwhites live together in coveys during fall and winter. These groups generally consist of remnants of several summer broods. In the evening the birds retire to their roosting ground where they have the unusual habit of forming a tight little circle on the ground, tails pressed together and heads toward the outside of the circle. Consequently, when disturbed, the whole covey bursts forth like an exploding grenade, to the confusion of the enemy.

In early spring when winter coveys break up, it suddenly becomes obvious how the Bobwhite Quail got its name. The male selects fence posts, low branches of trees, or stumps from which to send forth his bobwhite calls. Then he listens for a response.

53

Should he be fortunate enough to hear the soft answer of a female, with crest erect he flies to her, displaying all his charms by fluttering and strutting about her. Should a rival male answer a challenging call, however, a fast and furious fight may result. In the meantime, the pairing off process continues; the newly formed pair going steady for several weeks to a month before mating. At this time the male is very solicitous, even to the extent of bringing his mate choice tidbits to eat.

The nest is generally built by the male under supervision of the female. It is a simple affair consisting of a hollow scooped out in the ground along fence-rows, under brush piles, or in open fields and gardens. The nest is generally lined with dead grass, and dead and growing grass is woven into an arch over the nest, often leaving only a small opening on the side just large enough for the bird to enter. Sometimes nests consist of pine needles or other material.

Both sexes share in the task of incubating the 12 to 20 (usually 14 to 16) white eggs, which take from 23 to 24 days to hatch. The young leave the nest almost as soon as they are hatched; in fact, sometimes the chick runs off with part of the egg shell still clinging to it. The chicks are able to fly several yards a few days after hatching. Although bobwhites seldom have more than one brood a summer in the North, there may be two broods in the South.

The daily activities of bobwhites follow a definite pattern. They do not leave their nightly roosting place too early in the morning, preferring to wait until the rising sun has at least partially dried the grass. Then they fly to their feeding spot to feed for an hour or two, to be followed by a mid-day siesta, dusting, preening, or merely dozing. About two hours before sunset they search for food again before returning to roost at dusk.

Anyone wishing to learn more about the bobwhite should read H. L. Stoddard's classic *The Bobwhite Quail, Its Habits, Preservation, and Increase*.

Coturnix

Since so many people have recently been inquiring about a quail newly brought into this country, let us first of all decide how to pronounce its name. It is Coturnix, with accent on the "tur". Although this bird is a newcomer to North America, not even Americans whose ancestors came here on the Mayflower have a longer genealogical record. When Moses and the Israelites made their exodus from Egypt, the Lord sent them manna and quail which were probably the Coturnix.

This bird is the native quail of Central and Southern Europe, North Africa, and most of Asia. Our GI's became acquainted with this quail in Korea. There are about six different kinds of Coturnix, and at least ten subspecies.

Since many New Hampshirites can still remember the Bobwhite, a former native of this state, some comparisons might help. Whereas the Bobwhite weighs six to six and one-half ounces, the live weight of the smaller Coturnix is from four and one-half to five and one-half ounces. The female is slightly larger than the male. Coturnix do not covey up as do Bobwhites, neither do they run like the latter when hunted, consequently holding better for the bird dog. They usually flush in twos and threes, and fly about 100 to 200 yards before landing. They show a certain tendency to migrate; for this reason all states liberating these birds should band them so that the extent of movement may be determined.

The big difference between the Bobwhite and Coturnix is in the laying habits. We have very few species of birds in the United States so prolific as the Coturnix. On the day it hatches it is a tiny ball of fuzz about the size of a ping-pong ball. Only six weeks later it has already started laying eggs. At the age of eight weeks it is laying fertile eggs. Since it takes but sixteen days for these eight to fifteen speckled or brown mottled eggs to hatch, this quail can produce from two to three generations in one breeding season. Not only that, but the first offspring might already be laying that same summer. What eager beavers!

Many states, including New Hampshire, have been making trial plantings of the Coturnix to see what will happen.

Ken
Fagg

Rails

Probably only a rail hunter would know what sport there is in shooting so weak-flying a bird as a rail. On September 1 many states start their hunting season by opening up on rails and gallinules.

These birds, along with the American Coot, form a cosmopolitan group whose members are generally associated with marshes. The expression "thin as a rail" refers to their narrow bodies, long necks, and small heads which enable them to maneuver through dense growths of marsh plants. Their strong, long legs and toes help them walk with ease over the ooze and muck. When in danger they prefer to run into hiding and take to the wing only as a last resort, when they fly low over the marsh, legs dangling, and dropping abruptly back into the vegetation after a few rods of flight.

This group of birds is composed of about 180 different kinds. In North America there are ten species of rails (eighteen, if one takes the various subspecies into consideration), 2 gallinules, and 2 kinds of coots. They vary in size from the King Rail which reaches a length of about 19 inches, to the tiny Black Rail which is about 5 inches long. Six different species of these birds have been recorded in New Hampshire. The bill is short and henlike in the coots and gallinules, but fairly long and slightly curved toward the end in the rails. Noises made by the various members of this group somewhat resemble those of our barnyard fowl.

One of the commoner species, particularly in New Hampshire, is the Virginia Rail. This bird is very secretive in marshes; however, its pig-like grunting and squealing often gives it away. It slinks through the sedges and reeds in search of insects, snails and seeds, but it will also not hesitate to swim or dive after food. The nesting season starts about the middle of May and extends to about the beginning of July. Nests are shallow, basket-like structures built of dead leaves or stalks of marsh plants, and generally suspended a few inches above the water surface from stalks of emergent plants. Usually the surrounding vegetation is bent down and loosely intertwined over the nest to form an arch concealing the eggs. The clutches, averaging anywhere from 8 to 10 pale grayish or buffy white eggs, spotted with reddish brown and lilac, take somewhere between 18 and 22 days to incubate. After hatching the young are able to walk, swim, and dive. Adults temporarily lose power of flight while moulting during July and August.

American Coot

Although the American Coot is a member of the Rail Family, it has some rather "un-rail-like" characteristics. Unlike the so-called rails, the toes of the coot are furnished with lobes, and the hind toe has a flap; helping this bird to be an excellent swimmer and diver. While it most closely resembles a Gallinule, it is sufficiently duck-like so that many novice duck hunters bring home coots under the mistaken impression that they have shot real ducks. While coots can be eaten, they are not particularly palatable. Its habit of bobbing the head in time with foot movements when walking, and moving the head forward with each stroke of the foot when swimming, is a distinguishing trait of this bird. When alarmed, it does not take to the wing unless absolutely necessary, and when it starts to fly it seems to experience difficulty raising from the water, using feet and wings to do so.

The American Coot is a friendly bird, and where it is not heavily hunted it is apt to be quite unafraid of man. It is gregarious in feeding and nesting habits, but pugnacious in defense of its nesting territory. The sexes look alike. Its food consists primarily of vegetable matter, insects, mollusks, and an occasional fish.

In spring coots often arrive on their nesting territories before the ice is out. In fall they often wait until ice forms before migrating south. They nest among water plants around potholes and small ponds. The nests are floating structures but do not drift, since they are attached to reeds. The inner nest cavity, hollowed just enough to hold the eggs, is neatly lined with pieces of dried reeds or other smooth materials. The 8 to 12 buff colored, heavily spotted with brown, eggs are laid at the rate of one egg a day. Incubation, which takes about 21 to 22 days, is shared by both parents. The newly hatched young leave the nest immediately and are able to swim and dive shortly after emerging from the egg.

The American Coot is found in a large part of North and Central America, its range extending into the West Indies. Its breeding range is north to British Columbia, Ontario, and New Brunswick, and south to lower California, Texas and New Jersey, but not much on the Atlantic Coast. Although the Coot comes through New Hampshire during spring and fall, it is not known to nest here.

This Coot should not be mistaken for the scoter ducks so often called "Coots" along the Atlantic Coast in the northeastern states.

61

Snipes and Sandpipers

If you have difficulty telling the various snipes and sandpipers apart, think nothing of it. Even expert ornithologists have their troubles with these birds. There are about 100 different kinds found all over the earth, and about half of these are found in America. In fact, 24 different species of this group have been recorded in New Hampshire.

The snipes and sandpipers make up a family which belong to the Shore Bird or Wading Bird group. They usually have long soft-skinned bills. All nest on the ground with the exception of the European Green Sandpiper and the American Solitary Sandpiper. The young are generally able to leave the nest shortly after hatching.

Besides the many different so-called sandpipers, this group is also made up of Curlews, Yellow-legs, Godwits, Knots, Dowitchers, the Upland Plover (once an important game bird), the Woodcock, and various Snipes.

A well-known representative of the last group is the Wilson's Snipe. Often erroneously called a Jack Snipe, this bird with its fast, erratic flight is considered a fine game bird. Once it was very abundant but today its numbers have been greatly reduced. It occurs in nearly every part of North America, nesting from Alaska and northern Canada south to northern California, northern Illinois, and New Jersey. It winters as far north as unfrozen marshes, but mainly in the southern states, West Indies, and South America.

In the spring these snipes arrive soon after the frost is out of the ground. During their courtships they are apt to circle high overhead, swooping downward and producing a weird winnowing sound, resembling somewhat the noise made by a duck's wings in rapid flight and audible at a long distance. Both sexes probably participate in these demonstrations. Ornithologists are not certain whether the noise is made by the wings or the two pairs of outer tail feathers. The nest is a shallow hollow in the grass or moss. Three to four brownish or olive eggs, splotched and spotted with brown, are incubated by both sexes, taking from 18 to 20 days to hatch. The food of the Snipe consists of worms and insects.

Woodcock

Have you ever heard woodcock perform their courtship flight and song? This unique demonstration starts as soon as these birds return from the south, reaches a peak toward the end of April, and after May 15 declines rapidly. It is put on for about 40 minutes after sunset and again shortly before dawn from open fields or pastures, generally adjacent to alder thickets. Many people in the country have this "show" going on almost next to them without being aware of it. The male soars spirally to a height of two or three hundred feet, and then descends earthward by a series of fast zig-zag swoops accompanied by successive outbursts of liquid, gushing song which ends abruptly near the ground. The courtship flight also has a whistling sound made by currents of air through the three notched outer primary feathers of each wing. The time for each flight is usually slightly less than one minute. On the ground the woodcock then gives a harsh, nasal "peent", somewhat resembling that of a nighthawk. These courtship activities are thoroughly described in Pettingill's *The American Woodcock*, and a later publication by Mendall and Aldous titled *The Ecology and Management of the American Woodcock* presents a wealth of additional knowledge about this interesting game bird.

The woodcock's food consists mainly of earthworms, interspersed with some insects, seeds and berries. The female is generally larger than the male. Usually, but not always, the nest is built near water; generally in open, second-growth stands of timber with hardwoods predominating. There are generally four eggs (sometimes three or five) to a nest. There are no authentic data to show that more than one brood is raised in any one summer. The incubation period lasts about 20 to 21 days.

In September they start to migrate southward, travelling largely at night and seldom more than 50 feet from the ground. The bulk of the birds pass through New Hampshire in October. Locally raised birds often remain in the same cover late in autumn. Mendall reports two birds hatched from the same nest which were banded in May. Both were taken the last week in October by gunners from the same cover, within several hundred yards of where banded. Migration is leisurely — about 28 miles a day, even slower in fall. They winter in Maryland and Virginia, south to Florida, west to east Texas.

Terns

When we think of the ocean, we think of gulls and terns. In fact, so much are these two birds seen together, and so similar are they in their flight and habits that people often ask how to tell the two apart. The most obvious difference lies in the bill, the gull having a hooked beak while the tern has a straight, pointed one. In flight the gull's beak is generally pointed straight ahead while that of the tern is pointed downward. Terns are perhaps more graceful in flight; in fact, they are often called "Sea Swallows". Their manner of feeding differs from gulls, since terns are in the habit of hovering over the water and then plunging in to catch a fish.

There are about fifty different species of terns, of which fourteen inhabit North America, while six have probably been recorded in New Hampshire. They are more southern than gulls, only two species nesting north of Maine in eastern North America; and more migratory, none wintering on our coasts north of the Carolinas. Although most species are found off our coasts, some (like the Black Tern) nest only on freshwater.

One of the terns, occasionally seen off the New Hampshire coast, the Arctic Tern, is perhaps the world's migratory champion. It arrives in the far north about June 15, nesting to within eight degrees of the North Pole. It stays about 14 weeks to lay its eggs and raise its young. By about August 25 this tern heads for its winter home, which is in the Antarctic. Since it spends somewhat more time on its winter grounds than on its nesting grounds, it has approximately twenty weeks in which to make the 22,000 mile round trip. The Arctic Tern has more hours of daylight than any other animal on the globe, since it does not see the sunset for at least eight months out of the year.

Terns generally breed in large colonies, some species crowding their nests so close together on the ground that one finds it difficult to walk among the nests without stepping on them. Some species occasionally place their nests in trees. The majority lay 2 or 3 eggs, either white, greenish or yellowish with spots or blotches. The incubation period of the common tern, for instance, is 21 days. The downy young are dependent on their parents until they can fly.

Gulls

One of our most cosmopolitan groups of birds are the gulls. They belong to the so-called Order of Long-winged Swimmers. To this Order belong the Skua and Jaegers, Skimmers, Terns and Gulls. There are about fifty kinds of gulls distributed throughout the world, of which at least 23 have been recorded from North America, and nine from New Hampshire. Most of them breed north of the United States. The Laughing Gull is the only species which nests south of latitude 41° and is found nesting as far south as Texas and Louisiana.

As a rule it is difficult to tell one sex of gull from the other. Their winter plumage, however, differs somewhat from the summer plumage. In spring they exhibit courtship activities by strutting about, raising and lowering their heads, and from time to time emitting loud, sonorous notes at which time the head is raised, with bill wide open, until it points vertically upward.

Gulls are Nature's scavengers of waters, feeding on dying or dead fish, and on garbage in harbors. Franklin's Gull is well known in the midwest where it will follow the plow, feeding on insects. The California Gull is fond of field mice. In Salt Lake City, Utah, there is a monument to this gull "in grateful remembrance" of the time in 1848 to 1850 when this gull helped save the crops from a plague of crickets. On the other hand, gulls are also highly predaceous, readily feeding on the eggs and young of other birds.

Our most common gull is the Herring Gull. This species breeds from south-central Alaska to Cumberland Sound, south to British Columbia across the United States to Maine. It winters wherever there is open water in the north, southward to Lower California, Mexico and Cuba. Like all gulls, it nests in colonies. Nests are generally on the ground, consisting of mere depressions with scant nesting material, but occasionally are built in trees — generally bulky affairs of grass and moss. The three, light bluish, greenish or olive eggs, blotched and spotted, take from 24 to 28 days to hatch, with both sexes incubating. The newborn young are covered with down and are dependent on the parents until they can fly. Gulls do not have too many enemies. They are perhaps their own worst enemy, since many young are pecked to death by the adults. This probably happens when the young beg food off the wrong adult. Many young are also swept away by the surf.

Mourning Dove

Around 1945 mourning doves were still a rarity in New Hampshire. Today they are reported among the first spring arrivals from as far north as Berlin and Pittsburg, while they are not uncommon throughout southern New Hampshire during the summer months. When our Department raised buckwheat for deer in Bear Brook State Park several years ago, it was not unusual to flush over fifty doves from these fields.

Most southern states treat the mourning dove as a game bird. Its swift flight and delicate meat make it a prized sport among many hunters. Unless its population increases tremendously in our own state, however, I believe most of us will derive much more enjoyment from this dove just seeing it around and hearing its plaintive coo.

There are about 550 kinds of doves, of which only 17 species are found in the United States, and only the mourning dove in New Hampshire. The food of this bird consists mainly of grains, seeds, fruit and salt. A strange feature of doves is their manner of drinking. They immerse their bills to the nostrils, and the water is then drawn up in a continuous draft. This is probably unique among birds.

The nests of mourning doves are very simple, flat structures of sticks and straw, generally found fairly low in trees, in shrubs, and occasionally on the ground. As one man put it, "If doves spent more time building their nests, and less time billing and cooing, they would have better nests". This does not prevent them from bringing up two or three broods a summer. They lay one to two white eggs per nest, and it takes only about two weeks for these to hatch. The naked young are at first fed by a fluid, "pigeon milk", secreted in the crop of the adult, and later with moistened or partially digested seeds or grain from the parents' crop. In both cases the young one inserts its bill into the parent's mouth while the adult goes through violent jerkings of body and wings as it regurgitates its food.

short eared owl

saw whet owl

barred owl

snowy owl

barn owl

screech owl

great horned
owl

long-eared
owl

Ken
Fogg

Owls

Most of us in New Hampshire probably see no more than several owls a year and would be greatly surprised to know there are a good number of these night prowlers in the state. At least eight different kinds can be seen in New Hampshire, but only two — the Great Horned Owl and the Barred or Hoot Owl — can be considered as common throughout the year over the entire state, although the little Saw-Whet Owl is fairly common, particularly in northern New Hampshire. Both the Long-eared Owl and the Barn Owl are also suspected of nesting in our state, the former inhabiting mainly our evergreen forests and the latter generally nesting in abandoned buildings in extreme southern New Hampshire. The Short-eared Owl is occasionally observed in open lands during its migration. From time to time during winter months our state is invaded from the north by a white owl called the Snowy Owl. These visits seem to occur when there is a shortage of food in its native haunts. The Screech Owl also nests in New Hampshire and can be found in two color phases —some grayish and others reddish.

The Great Horned Owl is New Hampshire's largest and heaviest owl, with a wing spread of sixty inches. New Hampshire's smallest owl, the Saw-Whet Owl, has a wingspread of eighteen inches.

Owls usually lay their eggs in holes of trees or banks, or in deserted hawk or crow nests.

The farmer who experiences the destructive raid of a Great Horned Owl on his turkeys or poultry may find it hard to agree that owls, as a whole, are highly beneficial since insects, frogs, snakes, rodents, birds, and even skunks, make up the major portion of their food. Their prey is captured with their feet and they will swallow their food whole when it is not too large, later disgorging the hair and bones in the form of pellets. By studying these pellets, biologists have been able to learn a great deal about the food habits of the owls.

All owls in New Hampshire have yellow eyes, with the exception of the Barn and the Barred Owl, which have brown eyes. A person camping out for the first time may be scared out of his wits late some spring evening by the most unearthly hooting and caterwauling he has ever heard. Generally those awful noises come from a couple of male Barred Owls who are trying to determine which sings the prettiest.

Great Horned Owl

Many people will not suspect that at least one of New Hampshire's birds starts nesting in mid-winter. Our "tiger of the air", the Great Horned Owl, will at times start nesting as early as the latter part of January in mild winters. This bird has been found, covered with snow, setting on its eggs in sub-freezing temperatures of February. The nests are generally high up in large trees. Deserted hawk, crow, or squirrel nests are often used, although sometimes they may be in a hollow tree, and generally they are built of twigs, weed stalks, roots and feathers. It takes the two to three white eggs, often laid several days apart, about 28 days to hatch. The young stay in the nest about 6 to 7 weeks, and they cannot fly for at least 10 to 12 weeks. Some naturalists report that once the young are able to balance in the fork of the tree, the nest is destroyed by the parents so that the young remain inconspicuous.

Bones, hair, and feathers of their prey are regurgitated in the form of a pellet. The ground underneath their nests is generally littered with these pellets. By examining these one can determine fairly well what the owls have been eating. The Great Horned Owl is powerful, courageous, and bloodthirsty to the point of being savage. It flies silent as a shadow; and although it prefers to stalk its food at night it can also see well in daylight. If a particular individual acquires a preference for poultry, it can be highly destructive. Sometimes it will kill its prey and devour only the brains, leaving the flesh untouched. This two-foot long bird, sometimes with a five-foot wingspread, is powerful enough to kill a wide variety of animals. Woodchucks, skunks, squirrels, mice, hawks, snakes, fish, house cats and even porcupines are taken. Their staple diet is rabbits. They are also highly beneficial as attested by the remains of 113 rats found under one nest.

During mating season, they are apt to be noisier than normal. Their strong hoot may sound like a distant locomotive and again they may produce catlike squalls. One good way to find them is to listen for the commotion of many crows or jays for they like to gang up on an owl and pester the life out of him.

There are various varieties of horned owls, distributed from the arctic region in the North, through North, Central and South America to the Straits of Magellan in the South.

Woodpeckers

Although most of us try to avoid a chronic chiseler, New Hampshire has one well known group of chiselers who should be welcomed. At least five species of woodpeckers are common in our state: flicker, yellow-bellied sapsucker, hairy, downy and pileated woodpeckers. In northern Pittsburg, bird lovers occasionally come across two rare species — the Arctic and the American Three-toed woodpeckers. Once in a great while a red-headed woodpecker strays into our state.

Woodpeckers are found in all wooded portions of the world except Madagascar and Australia. There are about 425 species and subspecies, of which 45 are found in the United States. With the exception of the several species of 3-toed woodpeckers, they are all 4-toed (two point forward and two backward). This arrangement of toes, along with stiff tail feathers which can be pressed against the bark of trees to serve as a prop, enable these birds to climb trees with ease. As one would suspect, woodpeckers also have a stout beak with a chisel-shaped point. An extraordinary anatomical feature of these birds is the tongue, which is cylindrical in form and very long. The front end generally terminates in a hard point with barbs upon the sides, while the inside end splits in two. These two ends curl up around the back of the skull, in some species passing around the eye and in others entering the right nasal opening and extending to the end of the beak. This long tongue can be pushed out a considerable length, enabling the bird to probe for grubs or ants.

Woodpeckers rarely disfigure healthy trees. When they find a tree infested by wood boring larvae, however, they can locate these insects very accurately and will spend considerable time pecking for them. One exception is the yellow-bellied sapsucker, which has the bad habit of puncturing rows of holes in trees to start a run of sap. They then return to drink the sap and eat the insects there.

Their 4 to 8 white eggs are generally laid in cavities of trees. During the mating season woodpeckers, particularly flickers, are apt to be noisy. Their courtship consisting of nodding, bowing, swaying and chasing may seem ludicrous to us. As a whole, woodpeckers are a friendly lot. At times in spring when they pound away at hollow trees or eaves troughs early in the morning, we may wish they would be friendly somewhere else!

Canada Jay

If the truth were known, many of us who fish and hunt in extreme northern New Hampshire go there with the expectation of finding things more important than mere fish and game. Without fringed gentian, spruce grouse, crossbills, the quiet and fragrance of spruce and fir, and Canada Jays, the "North Woods" would soon lose their magic. Seldom does the Canada Jay fail to oblige. He seems to be as happy to see us as we are to catch sight of him. A good way to attract this jay is to fry your fish and bacon over an open fire. Quietly he appears out of nowhere, with an all consuming curiosity, which brings him almost within touching distance. Let not his stupid or vacant look deceive you, or you'll wonder where your bacon went. Many call him "Camp Robber". He is also known as "Moose Bird" or "Whiskey Jack". The latter name seems quite appropriate since he is apt to appear inebriated most of the time. Many individuals are so tame or greedy that they can be enticed to take bread out of the outstretched hand.

The Canada Jay ranges from the northern edge of coniferous forests in the Arctic, south into northern New England and west into northern Minnesota. Three close cousins — Rocky Mountain Jay, Alaska Jay, and Labrador Jay — are found in areas indicated by their names. In New Hampshire, Canada Jays are not common south of Pittsburg. Their calls and songs are many and varied. If one hears a noise in the north woods which cannot be ascribed to any other creature, a good guess will be the Canada Jay. Their food consists of insects, carrion, garbage, mice and berries. They are on other birds' black list, since they are nest robbers.

Nest construction starts in February, and these are therefore built very warmly, consisting of twigs, pine needles and bark lined with grass, feathers, moss and even spider webs. They are generally built in evergreen trees, such as spruce or cedar, and about six to twelve inches above the ground. The three to five pearl-gray eggs, speckled with brown, are laid about the middle of March. Incubation takes eighteen days. The young remain in the nest about two weeks, and then follow the parents around until June or July. Both parents take care of their fledglings.

Crow

Call them scoundrel, rascal, black devil, or just plain crow, it is still a pleasure to see them around in the dead of winter. To him who admires resourcefulness, the crow is a consistent source of wonder. Hardy enough to withstand the harshest New Hampshire winters, canny enough to thrive despite nationwide persecution, and plentiful despite its size and conspicuousness, this bird surely deserves our utmost respect. Nevertheless, it must be conceded that the crow is a thief to the point of being a kleptomaniac. Bright objects fascinate this bird, while small eggs of birds and large eggs of chickens will be taken with equal impunity. Anyone who has had a crow for a pet will admit that much this bird does seems to be due to either insatiable mischievousness or a blatant sense of humor. A pet crow of mine, Oswald by name, aroused the enmity of all neighboring housewives when he developed the habit of dropping Monday morning's wash on the ground by systematically removing the clothespins. A fast talking salesman was flabbergasted when a crow flew down on his shoulder, grabbed the pencil from his ear and then disappeared into the wild blue yonder. Only intimate acquaintanceship, however, revealed that Oswald had a more gentle side to him. When by himself where he thought no one observed him, he would begin to warble and sing a subdued gurgling song one could hardly associate with a crow.

Frogs, snakes, insects, fruit, and sprouting vegetation such as corn go to make up the crow's diet. Early in spring they begin to build their nests, generally high in trees. These are well-made — but coarse — of sticks, grass, tree bark, and often lined with the innerbark of dead trees, small roots, straw or hair. The 4 to 8 pale bluish or greenish eggs are blotched with brown and olive. The incubation period is about 18 days. The young are blind and naked and require about three weeks of care in the nest.

Our so-called Eastern Crow ranges through most of eastern United States westward to the arid region and northward to Newfoundland. In winter the northern limit of its range is slightly south of the Canadian border. At this time of the year it congregates in immense flocks called crow-roosts, at night, and forays out into the countryside during the daytime.

English Sparrow

According to the dictionary the word "exotic" means introduced from a foreign country. Consequently, when we talk about exotic plants and animals we refer to those which were not originally found in our country. Thistles, wild carrot, nightshade, cockroaches, Japanese beetles, house mice, Norway rats, carp, ring-necked pheasants, and the white man are some of the exotic species found in the United States. Some have proved highly detrimental while others might have proved to be a questionable asset.

The value of two exotics introduced during the last century remains debatable. In 1850 eight pairs of English Sparrows were brought to America for the first time and released in Brooklyn to control the cankerworm. More were released in later years. This specie thrived to such an extent that by 1900 it had spread from the Atlantic to the Pacific. Several factors favored this rapid spread. The English Sparrow is aggressive. As a race that tolerates no weaklings, competition for mates is vigorous, with few delicate social refinements. It is fairly tolerant of crowding and very adaptable. As a non-migratory group they are ready to start nesting in early spring, allowing time for up to three or more broods each season. Their nests are usually bulky affairs of grasses and other materials, almost invariably lined with feathers. They are found in gutter pipes, holes under the eaves, hollows in trees, and other such places. The fact that they weave fairly complicated nests indicates that these are not true sparrows, but belong to the weaverbird or Old World sparrow family. They lay from four to seven eggs, generally colored white and finely marked with olive. When the parents are ready to start a new brood, the fledglings are left to shift for themselves. These then form into flocks which constantly spread out into new territory.

The food habits of this sparrow are highly varied. Weed seeds, insects, fruit and grain are all grist for its mill. The house sparrow probably reached its peak population during the horse and buggy days. Today, its population has declined somewhat since it finds less food value in the exhaust fumes of cars.

This bird's value is of a questionable nature. It is cheerful but messy, it feeds on insects and also valuable fruit, and it steals nesting sites of other birds.

Starling

Another exotic species of doubtful value to our country is the starling. In 1890 some sixty of these were set free in Central Park in New York, and more were released the following year. By 1950 starlings had spread over most of the United States, some individuals appearing on the Pacific Coast. Fortunately, to date there is but one species found in our country. There are at least seventy different kinds distributed in other countries. It is not certain why they were ever brought here.

Since this bird is an early nester, often starting in the early part of April, it is generally able to produce two and sometimes as many as three broods by August. Although a hole-nesting species, it is less particular in choice of nest sites and in nest construction than are most native birds that build in cavities. Since it is partial to human association it may be found nesting in almost any sort of cavity about buildings. The nest itself is usually constructed of dry grasses, although straw, string, or cloth may be utilized. The interior is generally lined with a few chicken feathers.

The three to six eggs are pale blue. Incubation lasts about 12 days, and the young remain in the nest for two or three weeks. Soon after the first brood leaves the young gather in flocks, which grow rapidly in size. Late in August and early in September flocks numbering into the thousands may be seen in sections where the starling is common. In summer months there is practically no association between the juvenile birds and the adults during the day. At night both young and adult may occupy the same roost.

Many people living in cities, who may never have bothered giving our songbirds a second thought, have suddenly become bird watchers — mainly in self defense as they walked underneath the teeming roosting flocks. Being a size larger than the house sparrow the starling does things in just a little bigger way — the sparrow is noisy but the starling is noisier; in roosts the sparrow is smelly but the starling is smellier; and if the sparrow makes walking under a roost somewhat of a gamble, the starling makes it a real hazard!

Most ground feeding birds hop, but the starling walks. Half of its diet consists of animal food — mainly insects. Its forays on fruits and grains, and its competition with more valuable birds for nesting sites leaves much to be desired in the starling.

MAMMALS

Mammals in New Hampshire

There are sixty-four different kinds of wild mammals in New Hampshire, of which fifty-nine are distinct species. Among these are fourteen different kinds of mice and rats, eight kinds of bats, two kinds of moles, seven kinds of shrews, and three kinds of weasels. Two species, the wild boar and the elk, were recently introduced in this state.

The Opossum, common in the more southern states, is gradually invading New Hampshire. The northern-most record to date is of one caught in a trap in Lyman by Fred Girouard of Bethlehem. Fishers, once extremely rare and found mostly in northern New Hampshire, are increasing and spreading southward. They have recently been taken in Pembroke and in Hampton.

The last authentic record of a mountain lion (panther) in New Hampshire, despite many unconfirmed reports of later records, is one shot in the town of Lee in 1856. This specimen is now mounted in the Woodman Museum in Dover.

New Hampshire's largest mammal is the moose, with large specimens known to weigh as much as 1,400 pounds. Going to the other extreme, the state's smallest mammal is probably the pigmy shrew which seldom weighs more than one-ninth of an ounce and is found in the northern part of the state.

Although mammals are usually thought of as being restricted by nature to life on the ground or in trees, some have developed unusual features and abilities. New Hampshire has various examples, some common, others not so common, of this — bats that fly, flying squirrels which glide, moles with a star-shaped disk on their nose which tunnel under the sod, and water shrews that run on water.

The New Hampshire Fish and Game Department has a bulletin for distribution by Ralph G. Carpenter and Hilbert R. Siegler titled *A List of New Hampshire Mammals and Their Distribution*.

Opossum

Opossums, generally associated with country where persimmons grow, are spreading northward. Since 1945, when one was found in Gilmanton, these animals have been found in Keene, Warner, Jaffrey, and even Lyman.

Opossums are our only native North American Marsupial (mammals that carry their young in a pouch as do kangaroos) and should, therefore, be of more than passing interest to us. They are stupid animals with poor eyesight. They travel about mainly at night, relying on their sense of hearing, smell and touch. They are good climbers, using the tail as well as the feet to navigate along branches and vines. Although they can hang by the tail for a short time, they do not sleep in that position as often depicted. When cornered by an enemy they will often play dead. There are physiologists who now believe that the 'possum doesn't really play dead but that he actually faints from fright.

Opossums prefer to live along wooded waterways. During the day they curl up in hollow logs or trees, or in rocky dens. At night they sally forth to feed on insects, fruits, snakes, eggs, birds, and to raid hen houses. Most of the opossums are born in January and February in the South and somewhat later in the North. A second litter may be born in May or June. Birth is unusual. The gestation period is thirteen days and the young are born so prematurely and small that an entire litter of twenty can be carried in a teaspoon. At birth they crawl through the hairs of the mother, propelling themselves with their forefeet, and head straight for the pouch in which there are thirteen nipples. The first thirteen there attach themselves to these nipples and stay for about 50 to 60 days. Since there are no spare nipples, the remainder starve to death. When about the size of young rats the opossums crawl out of the pouch and are carried about by the mother as they cling to her back. Often one sees a picture of a mother 'possum with young ones on her back all neatly riding along with their tails wrapped around her tail. In the 17th Century a Dutch painter, Madame Merian, painted a picture of an opossum doing this, thereby starting a false legend which is still believed today.

A wealth of information may be obtained from Carl G. Hartman's book entitled *'Possums*.

Shrews

The smallest mammal in New Hampshire is the Pygmy Shrew. When full grown it weighs about 1/9 of an ounce. In fact, the smallest known mammal on earth is a tiny species of shrew. Seven different kinds of shrews have been found in our state. One, the water shrew, has the ability to run across quiet pools of water and to dive to the bottom of streams for its food.

When food bills begin to bother us let us be thankful we do not have the appetite of a shrew, for they eat from one to three times their weight in food each day. So fast does this animal burn up energy that it must hunt for food almost constantly, day and night, summer and winter. Their every move is quick and jerky, accompanied by series of twittering noises. Their appetite seems to be equalled only by their "shrewish" dispositions. When not butchering their own meals they fight with each other, and their fights are savage. When fighting, their feints and passes are almost too swift for the human eye. All this fast living seems to make for a short life, since they die of old age when they are about fourteen months old.

Their food consists of insects, slugs, centipedes, snails, earthworms, salamanders and carrion. Mice, although generally bigger than most shrews, are terrified in their presence, and well they might be. If a shrew gets hold of a mouse's tail it will immediately proceed to eat the poor creature alive. One reason it is able to do so is the presence of glands in the mouth which can excrete a poison similar to that of a cobra. This is particularly true of our short-tailed shrew. One shrew has enough poison to paralyze 200 mice.

Their nests, found in hollow stumps, under logs, or in burrows, are about 6 to 8 inches in diameter, ball-shaped affairs made of leaves and grass. The 3 to 10 (usually 6 or 7) naked young are about the size of honey bees. A shrew has from two to three litters a summer.

Shrews have a pair of glands, one on each flank, which secrete a strong-smelling musk which makes shrews distasteful to some predators. These tiny creatures resemble mice, at first glance, but on closer inspection their long snout, soft fur and "tobacco-stained" teeth show them to be different. In fact, they are more closely related to moles than to mice.

Moles

Like many a communist in this country, moles have gone underground. Although not nearly as destructive and treacherous as the former, the mole's activities occasionally conflict with man's interests — particularly on golf courses, lawns, and in gardens. However, by aerating the soil it does a vast amount of good. It feeds chiefly on worms and grubs, millipedes and centipedes, snails and slugs, insects and occasionally on vegetable matter.

There are five major groups of moles in the United States, of which two kinds are found in New Hampshire: the Hairy-tailed Mole and the Star-nosed Mole. There is perhaps no other mammal known with such a strange star-shaped fringe on the snout as has the Star-nosed Mole with its 22 pink, fleshy projections. Another unusual feature about this mole is that the tail of many individuals swells to several times its normal thickness during the winter. No one knows why.

The fur of moles can be brushed in both directions, enabling them to move backward and forward in their tunnels. While their hind legs and feet are small, their short front legs with broad shovel-like feet are stout and muscular. These are used to dig two kinds of tunnels: a deeper set between six inches and two feet beneath the surface where the mole lives in winter and very dry weather; and the surface tunnel so apparent in lawns, used chiefly as a means for reaching food. This one may sometimes be as much as one-half mile long. Tunnels are generally found in soft, moist soil having considerable humus. The Star-nosed Mole has burrows in swampy places, often ending in stream banks, since this mole is a good swimmer. When moles dig their tunnels they probably use their snouts to probe the earth ahead. Then the big front feet are used to shovel the dirt aside, while it twists the forward part of its body sideways and also pushes upward with the forefeet. In compact soil they move ahead about fifteen feet an hour. The "molehills" (not to be mistaken for tunnels) consist of dirt pushed out of the lower and deeper tunnels.

Moles breed once a year — in March. After a gestation period of about six weeks the one to five young are born in a chamber lined with leaves and grass in the lower tunnel. They are almost full grown in two months and mature the following spring, and by the time they are three years old they have one foot in the grave.

Bats

Of the many species of bats distributed widely throughout the world at least eight different kinds have been recorded in New Hampshire. The two most common are the little brown bat and the big brown bat. The one most frequently seen is the big brown bat.

Although a host of superstitions surround bats, they do have enough peculiar habits to give them a legitimate claim for a high position among nature's oddities. They are, for instance, the only mammal capable of sustained flight. Furthermore, they can "see" without use of their eyes. When in flight they continually utter high-pitched, often ultrasonic, squeaks and are guided by the returning echoes. So efficient is this method that bats, with their eyes gummed shut, released in a roomful of hanging ropes, have been able to fly at top speed through intricate mazes and avoid colliding with the ropes.

While different bats eat a variety of foods which include fruit, fish, and in the case of the vampire bats, blood, the New Hampshire species are insectivorous. Perhaps this insect diet explains why bats sometimes swoop very close to the heads of people who are outdoors in late evening with a swarm of mosquitoes hovering about. The insects are caught either in the jaws or the tail membranes of the bat. On a quiet night if a bat is very close the snapping of the teeth is quite audible.

Most active in late evening and early morning, the bats sleep in caves, crevices, hollow trees or any place where they are protected from the weather — such as under the eaves of buildings.

Although they mate in the fall, fertilization does not take place until the following spring when one or two young are born. The young are carried about by the mother on her nightly forays. Bats are not simply "flying mice" as some people may think. In fact, they are not even close relatives of the rodent. Bat's teeth resemble those of the cat family rather than members of the gnawing tribe.

Cottontail

The true rabbits are composed of about 60 to 70 species and subspecies of so-called Cottontails, of which only one, the New England Cottontail, is found in New Hampshire.

The Cottontail seems to thrive on adversity. Practically anything that eats meat will eat rabbits. Hunters annually harvest more cottontails in the United States than any other game animal, although surprisingly, in New Hampshire this animal is fairly low on the sportsmens' list. While a cottontail has been known to reach the age of eight years, few are fortunate enough to live longer than a year. Despite it all, rabbits can be found practically anywhere in the southern part of North America where the country is not too heavily forested. They are common in most of our State except in northern Coos County. What keeps them going? The answer lies in their — what biologists call — high reproductive capacity.

Have you ever come across two rabbits facing each other, as if to start a fight, when one suddenly dashes at the other, who in turn leaps into the air as the first one plunges by underneath? Well, they weren't fighting. After about two days of this courtship, the female gets tired of it all and drives the male away. About a month later, the female can be found digging a shallow depression in the ground, about the size of a small cake, lining it with grass and patches of fur which she pulls out of her underside. This might take place several days before the event, and when it happens the mother may be in some other part of her territory. In that case, she will carry her litter of about 4 to 7 blind and naked young to the nest, cover them with grass and fur and then return only at intervals to feed the babies. In about a week their eyes open, and a few days later they venture short distances from the nest to feed. Within two weeks of birth, the young leave their nest for good. In the meantime, the mother may have mated again and thus is capable of producing about 4 to 5 litters a year. And within about six months her babies in turn become rabbit factories.

If a particular rabbit becomes a nuisance in your garden, try him in your skillet as "Hasenpfeffer".

Snowshoe Hare

The hare hunter's complaint against cottontails is their habit of going into holes when pursued, whereas snowshoe hares, with their big hind feet and fur-covered toes, are better equipped to run across snow and seldom disappear down holes. They are fast, too. At top speed they can clear ten feet a leap and make four leaps a second. From that you should be able to figure out how many miles they can run per hour. Their habit of changing from brown in summer to white in winter — from whence their name of varying hare — is also to their advantage in snow. In his excellent study of the snowshoe hare in Maine, Joye Harold Severaid determined that this hare's color change occurs during moulting — a process which takes about seventy-two days.

These hares are homebodies. Some spend their entire life within a hundred yard radius. In thick, brushy woods their range is about 20 to 30 acres, and about 60 acres in open woods. They mature in one year and have been known to reach the ripe old age of nine years, although seldom do they become this old in the wild. While they are found in all types of forest habitat and throughout the State except along the Coast, they seem to prefer softwood swamps, willow-alder swamps, or fir thickets. Much of the day, particularly during inclement weather, they rest in so-called forms, generally on small, dry knolls or under fallen trees. In the summer they like to relax in dusting places.

The males average somewhat less in weight than the females. The heaviest hare recorded by Severaid in his studies reached a weight of slightly over four pounds. Since the male snowshoe hare is sterile during the winter months, breeding courtships do not ordinarily take place until the month of March. Gestation is from 35 to 40 days, and the day the young are born the female usually mates again. The mother hare gives birth to her two or three young wherever she happens to be. The fully furred young are born with their eyes open and can walk the first day. Since these hares average about three litters a summer, they generally produce about 7 to 9 young a year. This must be sufficient to perpetuate their kind, since the snowshoe hare is a classic example of an animal that periodically builds up tremendous populations then practically disappears, only to start another upsurge in numbers.

Woodchuck

The main trouble with groundhog day in our state is that it comes several weeks too early. Chances are that every last woodchuck in New Hampshire sleeps right through February 2. Around March 2, however, the males begin to sally forth — not to look for sunshine or clouds but for female woodchucks. The ground may still be covered with snow, so their tracks can be observed wandering from one den to another. Often the paths of males cross and then there ensues a gnashing of teeth and an ear-chewing brawl. About four weeks after these affairs of the woodchuck world have been settled, two to six blind, naked young are born, each weighing about an ounce. These remain in the den about four weeks until their eyes open, then they come forth to begin feeding on young fresh grass. By July they leave their parents to establish their own shallow burrows.

The burrows of mature woodchucks sometimes sink to a depth of five feet and may extend 30 or more feet. One or more of the chambers terminate in blind sacs which are generally higher than the main runways so that water will not rise into them. These sacs usually have grass or leaf nests in them. The conspicuous thing about woodchuck homes is the fresh mound of dirt at the main entranceway. Many a boy and his dog, dashing to cut off the 'chuck from his main hole, have been perplexed to see their quarry disappear down inconspicuous "plunge holes" which were dug from within so that no mound could be seen.

Woodchucks live mainly on succulent greens and fruits. By late September they have put on quite a layer of fat and when the first heavy frost comes they crawl into their burrows, roll up in a ball with head between hind legs, and front paws together and around their shoulders. Breathing slows down, pulse becomes faint, and body temperature drops down to between 43° and 57° F. This is true hibernation. During this time the body fat is used up and the animal may lose one-third to one-half of its weight.

Although most farmers may disagree, the groundhog has many good qualities. Rabbits use their dens as homes. Ten percent of New Hampshire's hunters enjoy stalking woodchucks with binoculars and guns, and many consider the meat very tasty.

Squirrels

In the United States there are five kinds of tree squirrels: red squirrels, gray squirrels, fox squirrels, tassel-eared squirrels, and flying squirrels. These have numerous subspecies. New Hampshire harbors three kinds — flying, red, and gray squirrels. The latter is the only one of importance as a game animal.

The big mystery is why the common gray squirrel does not play a more important role as a game animal in New Hampshire. In many states it ranks first in importance, while in this state only 11% of the resident hunters and 6% of the nonresident hunters seek this animal. When one considers its delicacy in a stew, its abundance in southern New Hampshire, and its craftiness once it is subject to hunting pressure, the mystery deepens. Helenette Silver, Biologist for the New Hampshire Fish and Game Department, points out that this squirrel was protected from all hunting in New Hampshire from 1915 to 1935. She believes that sportsmen simply lost the squirrel hunting habit. Perhaps the squirrel will gradually increase in popularity as a game animal with the coming of new generations of hunters.

In New Hampshire the gray squirrel breeds in mid-winter. The gestation period is about 44 days, so that the one to four young are usually born sometime in March. There is another upsurge in litters in late summer. The mother takes the entire responsibility for care of the young while the father is out two-timing with other females. Generally born in cavities of trees, but sometimes in leafy nests in tree tops, the young remain blind for about five weeks. When disturbed the mother may carry them considerable distances. In transit the young wrap their tails and legs around their mother's neck. Most wait until their second year to mate.

Their food consists of nuts, buds, fruits, berries, corn, and insects. The squirrel's chief enemies are great horned and barred owls, foxes, bobcats, some hawks and martens.

A strange habit of squirrels is their periodic tendency to start on mass migrations, generally when they have increased to large numbers. During Colonial days these migrations were often spectacular, participated in by many thousands. Today these are by smaller numbers. A few years ago such a mass movement took place across Massabesic Lake. Large numbers drowned and were found along the shores.

Flying Squirrels

From time to time boys become the proud foster parents of young flying squirrels. As these boys undoubtedly discover, flying squirrels become affectionate pets. Their main drawback is the fact that these animals prefer to sleep during the day and become active after dusk.

There are two varieties in New Hampshire — the small eastern flying squirrel and the larger Mearn's flying squirrel. Some naturalists maintain our woodlands have more flying squirrels than red squirrels, but few people realize how numerous they really are. During the day they den up in hollow trees or in abandoned leaf nests of other squirrels. They seem to prefer woodpecker holes, particularly those of the downy woodpecker. Their nightly activities are generally restricted to an area of about four to five acres.

Sociable creatures, several may share a crowded nest during the day. As many as fifty have been found together in one tree cavity. Their method of locomotion is unusual for mammals. Climbing to the top of a tree they leap into the air and spread their four legs apart, which stretches out the fine fold of fur-covered skin found on each side of the body and enables them to glide from one tree to another and as far as 150 to 300 feet. Their sail through air is in a descending curve which can be turned at right angles from the line of flight through use of the tail, which acts as a rudder. As they approach their destination they raise their head and land feet first.

They breed late in February or early March. After a gestation period of forty days, two to six blind, naked young are born. There may be another litter in July or August. In about four weeks the young open their eyes, and not until they are six to eight weeks old do they begin to make short glides. The first five weeks their only food is the mother's milk. She is extremely devoted and fearless. The father is not permitted to see the young while they are tiny. If something happens to a nest of young ones the mother rolls each baby into a ball, grasps it by the slack skin of the belly and carries it away.

Flying squirrels eat berries, fruits, mushrooms, nuts and even young birds. Their main enemies are predatory birds and mammals — especially house cats — and man, who destroys their homes when he chops down hollow trees.

Chipmunk

On warm pleasant days in March you may see an inquisitive little chipmunk scurrying along stone walls and through shrubbery. This is the male chipmunk in search of a mate. The baby chipmunks are born thirty-two days after mating. Most litters number four or five, but there may be as many as six, or as few as two. At birth the "chippies" are tiny red beings, entirely hairless and almost transparent. At one month their eyes open and, except for size, they are now quite like their parents. When three months old they have their permanent teeth and are probably set adrift to fend for themselves.

The chipmunk may spend its life within two or three acres. A suitable house is important, however. The chipmunk first digs almost straight down four or five inches, then slopes off a little, but still descends until it reaches a depth of about three feet. The shaft, about two inches in diameter, frequently twists about in its underground course. During the four or five years of its average normal life the chipmunk remodels and extends its home until the tunnel is thirty or more feet long, has several entrances, a number of short spur tunnels, and up to six rooms — including two or three small store rooms. This animal is found throughout New Hampshire.

Their diet consists mainly of fruits and seeds of a great variety of plants; seeds of many annuals; and nuts such as acorns, walnuts, and hazelnuts. In the summer the chipmunk gobbles quantities of berries — blackberries, blueberries, etc. It also eats June bugs, wireworms, cutworms and other insects which harass the gardener. Not to its credit however, is that it has been known to take birds' eggs and nestlings. Food may be stored in several places. Filling its cheek pockets the chipmunk darts to a storage place, spilling the food by squeezing the cheek pockets with its paws in back-to-front motions. The earth is then replaced and camouflaged with leaf litter.

Its enemies include snakes and weasels (which can come right into the tunnels), foxes, bobcats, hawks, owls, house cats, automobiles, and small boys with slingshots and .22's.

In late October the chipmunk retires to its home. During the really cold periods it goes "dead to the world", rolling up like a hoop with its head tucked between its hind legs and the tail thrown over the back and head. It becomes cold and stiff and its blood pumps very slowly. During warm spells, however, it awakens, nibbles at its store of food, and may even take a little run if the sun is bright.

Porcupine

Although many people call our porcupine a hedgehog this is a misnomer. There is an animal in Europe known as hedgehog, which has spines like our porcupine, but there the resemblance ends. The true hedgehog is an insectivore while our porcupine is a rodent.

The outstanding characteristic of the "porky" is, of course, its coat of spines, which can number anywhere from twenty to thirty thousand, and vary in length from ½″ to 5″. The question often arises as to whether these animals can throw their quills. Victor Cahalane, author of *Mammals of North America* writes: "Not ordinarily . . . . An old quill may be attached so loosely to the tail that, when the appendage gives a mighty flip, the quill may be thrown as much as five or six feet. This flying dart may strike the enemy with enough force to penetrate the skin . . . . Such an occurrence is pure luck. The porcupine has no control over it, and it does not happen often."

These animals weigh anywhere from ten to twenty pounds when adult. They can swim, and in summer can often be found around ponds feeding on lily stems and roots. They also like corn, apples, bones, green leaves, and anything with salt on it. Their main diet, particularly in winter, consists of the inner bark of trees — especially hemlock and spruce.

The breeding season begins in late October and lasts until early December. The gestation period lasts 209 days, approximately as long as that of the deer. Usually one young is born, with open eyes, weighing about one pound — twice the weight of newborn black bears. The newly born young are well-clothed with fur and even at birth the sharp points of the small quills can be felt. The mother often begins to wean its offspring within a week. They can climb the second day after birth, but spend most of their early days sleeping in logs, stumps, etc. Enemies of "porkys" are the red fox, bobcat, and especially fishers.

Porcupines look stupid but are actually quite intelligent. Sometimes they make affectionate pets. Occasionally they play by standing up on their hind feet and doing kind of a rock-and-roll dance. Anyone lost in the woods should not hesitate to eat "porkys", since their meat can be quite tasty. They occur in wooded areas of the entire state.

Beaver

The beaver has played a most important role in the history of New Hampshire. The fur trade was of paramount importance in the original economy of the early settlers and the beaver, once found in practically every town in New Hampshire, was finally trapped to extinction. About 1914 they started coming back into New Hampshire from Maine. By protecting them and transplanting them into southern New Hampshire they gradually increased and are now, once more, found in most of the state.

Much is still not known about this animal. Do they mate for life or are they polygamous? What is the purpose of the split second-claw on each hind foot? It is generally believed that this adaptation is used for combing the fur and removing lice from the fur and wood slivers from the teeth. Why do they seem to become ill when their tail remains dry for too long a period of time? Are the mud pies which beaver make used primarily as communication spots for other beaver? But much has also been learned about them. An intensive study recently completed by a group of workers in Maine and written up by biologists Hodgdon and Hunt disclosed that beaver usually mate towards the end of their second year. Breeding generally takes place between January and March, reaching a peak in mid-February. Gestation is about 100 days, with most of the young being born the latter part of May. Beaver give birth to one litter a year, averaging 3.15 young per litter. The young weigh about one pound at birth and are fully developed, being able to swim but unable to dive because of air caught in their fur. The young normally remain in their lodge for one month after birth.

Adult beaver average about forty pounds in weight and can swim from one-fourth to one mile under water, staying under as long as fifteen minutes.

A colony of beaver consists of a family group. If unmolested the group generally consists of the two adults, the young of the previous year (yearlings), and young of the current year (kits). The yearlings generally leave home the beginning of their second year during the time their second batch of brothers and sisters are being born. The 647 beaver censused in Maine had up to fourteen individuals per colony, and average 4.3 per family.

Answers to the question of whether beaver are a liability or an asset to the State of New Hampshire would probably be quite

varied. The timber lot owner will be unhappy if his trees are flooded, but thankful to have a water hole handy in case of fire. The highway crews will curse the beaver who dams up their culverts. The fisherman who comes upon a remote beaver pond and snags out of it some of the fattest trout he has ever caught in that particular stream will disagree with the other fisherman who has seen his stream so choked with dams that trout could not negotiate it on their spawning runs, or warmed up to the extent that suckers and shiners took over. Hunters often head for the small openings produced by beaver to look for woodcock, grouse, deer, and especially ducks. The trapper will see dollar bills everytime he looks at a fresh beaver impoundment. Beaver impoundments also attract muskrats, mink, raccoons, and otter.

To manage beaver, therefore, three objectives should be kept in mind:

1. A maximum of benefit to other furbearers, game and fish.
2. A maximum harvest of prime pelts.
3. A minimum of damage to property and fishing waters.

The most effective management measure is proper trapping — sufficient to keep property damage to a minimum, restricted enough to permit beavers to maintain their populations, and at a time when pelts bring in the most money.

Maine beaver pelts were found to be the most prime during the last two weeks in February, all of March, and the first week in April. From a money standpoint, therefore, the trapping season should take this into consideration. There is another factor to be remembered. Beavers are restricted to the privacy of their family domain at breeding time. If one of the mated pair is trapped during the winter, the remaining adult has no opportunity to seek another mate — thus no reproduction. Thus, trapping after the peak of the breeding season (mid-February) would seem most logical, since trapping before that time results in a considerable number of barren adult females.

Muskrat

The muskrat rates as the number one furbearer in the United States. Although not in income, in numbers taken it also ranks first in New Hampshire. From 1950 to 1959, for instance, a total of 126,772 "rats" grossed trappers almost $147,000. Many a farm boy has probably earned his first gun through the trapping of this furbearer; and has thereby also helped many a fair maid acquire her Hudson Seal fur coat.

Most of us are familiar with the muskrats dome-shaped house of cattails and sedges which spot our marshes. Less familiar are the homes of muskrats built in creek and river banks. These are dens generally well above the water line, but with entranceways or exits which the "rats" have burrowed underneath the surface of water, well-hidden from the view of their enemies. A recent publication by Maurice M. Alexander, titled *The Muskrat in New York State,* available from the State University of New York College of Forestry, Syracuse, New York, describes these dens and presents various suggestions for managing this furbearer.

The muskrat is prolific, a fact which should not be surprising when one considers its annual mortality from enemies and other causes. Marsh hawks, owls, foxes, and large turtles take a heavy toll. The mink is one of its most deadly persecutors. When natural predation does not keep populations within bounds and overcrowding occurs, there is considerable fighting in which a number die from the wounds of battle. Floods drown out the baby rats, and droughts cause starvation. Then there are the trappers. Despite it all, muskrats remain an abundant animal.

They have about three litters of young a season, the first one in April or early May, after a gestation period of about 29 or 30 days. Litters contain anywhere from one to eleven young, and each baby rat, when born, weighs not quite an ounce.

The muskrat gets its name from the fact that it has two musk glands. These enlarge during the breeding season, giving off a secretion which many claim has a rather pleasant odor. These furbearers are able to mate when they are about nine or ten months old. Although the young are but an ounce in size at birth, they grow rapidly and can start to swim when ten days old. In less than thirty days they are driven from their home by their

117

mother to shift for themselves. This is a biological necessity since another litter is due about that time. Often the young are born on a feeding lodge. The mother then transfers the young, one by one, grabbing them by the skin of the belly and swimming to the permanent lodge.

Muskrats are mainly vegetarians. The roots and stalks of cattails are a favorite, although rushes, arrowheads, and numerous other aquatic plants are eaten. Corn is a delicacy. Clams and crayfish are also eaten in considerable quantities. Since the availability of food in mid-winter can become a matter of life or death, stream bank muskrats are inclined to be anti-social so far as their homes are concerned. Occasionally, in winter several will stay in one house for warmth. In fact, as many as twenty-five were found in one den. However, as a rule muskrats prefer to be alone. In marshes where food is less of a problem, houses will average about four or five rats.

How can we maintain muskrats at optimum populations? Control of water levels and proper harvest are the two most important management tools. Most of the waterfowl areas developed by the New Hampshire Fish and Game Department are also proving ideal for muskrats, since we try to flood a maximum amount of territory with water less than two feet in depth — a depth conducive to the growth of aquatic plants. While we thus furnish food for muskrats, they return the favor by uprooting plants and opening up areas for ducks. Under ideal conditions a rat population can "run wild" in short order. This immediately brings on a counteracting process on the part of Nature, so that all excess rats soon perish. To avoid such waste we recommend that trappers harvest them. It is good management to harvest about half the rats each winter. To determine their number, count the houses in a marsh (not the small feeding platform, but the larger "live" houses) and multiply by four. If the take is correct, the number of houses will remain about the same.

Rat

No animal in New Hampshire is so bad but that we find some good in it. We are hard put, however, to do this for the Norway, the common house rat. No other animal in the United States is so important from the standpoint of destruction to human life and property. Since a pair of rats will eat the equivalent of a 100-pound sack of grain in a year it becomes obvious how much it annually costs us to support the many millions of these creatures. They kill poultry and other domestic animals. They contaminate man's food. They carry communicable diseases such as bubonic plague, murine typhus, infectious jaundice, rat-bite fever, trichinosis, spotted fever, scarlet fever, typhoid fever, diphtheria, tularemia, and rabies. Not long ago papers reported an attack by rats on a baby in its crib in Concord (1956).

The Norway rat is world-wide in distribution, living almost everywhere man has settled. It first appeared in the eastern United States about 1775 and reached the Pacific Coast about 1851. The fewest rats are found in well-kept and clean areas.

These rats commonly dig tunnels in the ground to depths of 1½ feet and averaging about 3 feet in length. The network of tunnels has one or more main entrances, and several emergency holes which are kept covered with shallow soil or weeds. As we all know, they also make their homes in buildings. In large cities rats remain all year in the same locality, and probably stay within 100 to 200 feet of their nests. Around villages and farms they tend to leave man's habitation in spring and invade the fields where they breed and feed. In the fall most return to live around man's dwellings.

Norway rats breed all during the year but the heaviest production occurs in spring and fall. The gestation period lasts from 21 to 26 days; and a female rat averages about five litters a year, although some have as many as 12 litters in a year. From 2 to 22 young may be born in one litter, but the average is from 7 to 11. At birth the young are naked, and remain blind from 14 to 17 days. They are weaned at about three weeks. Although some mature as early as 28 days of age, most do not mature until they are between 3 and 5 months old.

If it were not for hawks, owls, snakes, skunks, weasels, foxes, minks, and other carnivores, our war with rats would be a much more serious problem.

Red Fox

A good way to start a first-rate argument among New Hampshire residents is to discuss the merits of the red fox. Much will depend on whether one happens to be talking to a farmer, a bird hunter, or a fox hunter. The least one can say for the fox is that he is loved and hated with equal intensity.

Cunning Reynard lives by his wits rather than brawn and seems able to maintain himself despite intense persecution. The red fox seems more adaptable to situations than his smaller cousin, the gray fox. While the latter is more an animal of swamps and forests, the red fox has learned to adjust himself to life in forests, on prairies, around farms, and even in cities. Dogs find the red fox a much more cunning quarry than they do the gray. The one thing the gray can do better than the red is climb trees.

Both species are found in New Hampshire, the red being common throughout the state while the gray is uncommon and found mainly in southern New Hampshire. The red weighs between 8 and 12 pounds, although a heavy individual may tip the scales at 14 pounds. The gray weighs between 7 and 11 pounds, with some individuals weighing more. Males outweigh the females.

The breeding season of the red fox starts toward the end of winter, when one can hear his high-pitched barking at night. The 4 to 10 young are born 51 days later in a den under stumps or in remodelled woodchuck burrows. About five weeks later the pups come to the entrance of the den where they tumble and play like ordinary puppy dogs. They are tended and fed by both parents, which stay mated for one season, until the family breaks up about August.

The foxes' main enemies are dogs, farmers, trappers, and bobcats. Their food is very diverse, consisting of mice, rabbits, birds, carrion, woodchucks, muskrats, snakes, turtles, berries, apples, frogs, grasshoppers, chickens, and sometimes even porcupines. They like to cache food not needed for immediate use.

To avoid deportation the author insists on remaining anonymous when making the following unequivocal statements: 1) reducing the fox population will not increase our grouse or pheasant populations, 2) fox populations remain healthiest when subjected to constant persecution, and 3) the poorest way to keep foxes in check is through bounties.

Gray Fox

In recent years the gray fox has gradually been extending its range northward. As a result, each spring during this fox's mating season, the New Hampshire Fish and Game Department receives various telephone calls from people who have seen "rabid acting" foxes. Fortunately, these strange-acting foxes were probably more lovesick than rabid.

There are two species of gray foxes in the United States. The one we occasionally find in New Hampshire is commonly found in southern and eastern North America, south through Mexico into northern South America. Then there is a much smaller species found on the Pacific Coast islands off of southern California. Our gray fox is slightly smaller than the red fox. Although individuals have been recorded weighing 19 pounds, the gray generally weighs somewhere between 7 and 11 pounds. Unlike its cousin the red fox, which likes to live around farms, the shy and retiring gray prefers wooded areas and swamps. The fox hunter prefers the much more cunning red fox to the gray, since the latter does not run far when pursued, preferring to den up or to climb trees, at which it is fairly adept. Its yapping bark, repeated four or five times, is louder than that of the red fox.

The gray fox is generally monogamous although some cases of polygamy occur. The mating season takes place between January and May, probably reaching a peak in northern United States during March. At this time the males often have vicious fights. The gestation period is somewhere between 50 and 63 days, probably averaging about 53 days. After birth of the one to seven blind and almost naked young, both parents take care of them. They are good parents. In fact, the female has been known to bare her teeth and growl at humans when they have approached a den of young ones. They will move their young to a new location when disturbed.

By the time the young are 16 weeks old they can take care of themselves; and they are full grown when about twenty-five weeks of age. Rabbits, birds, small rodents, snakes, eggs, fruits and nuts make up their diet.

If man and his dogs, bobcats, and eagles do not interfere, they live to the ripe old age of about five years.

Black Bear

According to Victor H. Cahalane, author of *Mammals of North America,* the black bear resembles man more than any other North American mammal. He has some of man's best traits, and some of his worst. Ordinarily the bear is an independent creature that works hard for a living and generally minds his own business. He can stand, swim, and climb trees. His physical resemblance to man is most noticeable when the skin is removed. Bears which have become tame can be inveterate beggars, or robbers, or clowns that love applause. They can be very sociable, and may develop a craving for pie, cake, and soft drinks. The mother trains her cubs with affection and severe discipline (perhaps using better judgment than many modern human mothers).

The black bear is found in practically all of wooded North America, including portions of Mexico. Some are found in every state of the union except Rhode Island, New Jersey, and Kansas. They range in color from black to pale cinnamon, and usually have a white spot on the chest. An adult ranges in length from 4½ to 6½ feet, and between 24 and 40 inches in height at the shoulders. They usually weigh between 200 and 300 pounds, although an exceptional individual may go as high as 500 pounds.

Male and female bears have nothing at all to do with each other except for about a month each year in the early part of the summer. Females do not breed until they are three years old, and generally have but one cub the first time. Thereafter, like deer, they usually have twins, and sometimes triplets, but rarely four young ones.

When cold weather sets in the bear becomes drowsy. Once he has had plenty to eat he will "hole up". In the south this lasts only a few days or a week at a time, while in New Hampshire it may last from sometime in November to April, depending on weather, snowfall, sex, and food conditions. This is not true hibernation, however, since the bear's temperature remains normal and he may even come forth from time to time during warm spells. Their winter home may be a den, a cave or ledge among broken rocks, hollow logs, windfalls, or often even right in the open under a dense crown of conifer. Pregnant females are apt to be more careful in selecting wintering beds than the males.

When bears are born, the blind, hairless little cubs are about nine inches long and weigh out half-a-pound. They are generally born about January. While the mother dozes on, her tiny cubs know where to find their meals and eat, sleep, and grow. After about forty days they open their eyes and begin to cut their teeth. When they emerge from their den about three months after birth, they may weigh from five to eight pounds. Usually the cubs travel with the mother throughout the first year and even den with her the first winter after birth. Since it seems that bears usually breed every other year, there is apt to be little conflict in this arrangement.

When the mother and her cubs leave the den in spring they do considerable roaming around, covering perhaps a radius of ten miles. The solitary male probably has a home range of about fifteen miles. When they become tired they sleep wherever they happen to be. A large bear can relax completely when sprawled lengthwise on a limb only four inches in diameter. His legs hang down on each side and he sleeps soundly without falling off. When in a hurry a bear can travel as much as twenty-five miles an hour for short distances.

Bears spend a good deal of their time looking for food. They will eat practically anything that looks, smells, or tastes like food, including insects, fruit and berries, nuts, fish, carrion, mice, garbage in town dumps, and even grass and sedge. In a bulletin entitled *The Black Bear and its Status in Maine,* recently published by the Maine Department of Inland Fisheries and Game, Howard Spencer states that only a little over 8% of all food found in bears examined in Maine was animal matter.

Occasionally an individual bear will discover it can obtain an easy meal by killing livestock. Since the habit, once developed, stays with that bear, it is best that such an animal be destroyed.

Bears have a peculiar habit of establishing "marking posts". Natives often call them "bear trees". A bear will stand up, reach as high as he can, and claw the tree. Some people think this is a measuring post on which passing bears record their reach. The real purpose of these trees is not known, however.

Raccoon

Next of kin to the bear in New Hampshire is the raccoon, an intelligent and courageous animal. The coon's technical name is *lotor*, which means "the washer" and was derived from this animal's habit of dunking its food in water, even such items as crayfish or frogs which just came from there. When water is not nearby the coon will devour its food without performing this usual ritual. Its actual purpose is debatable. Victor Cahalane, author of *Mammals of North America,* writes that many naturalists believe raccoons are dunking rather than washing their food and thereby derive pleasure from feeling it under water through their sensitive hands.

The raccoon is found in every state of the Union, in southern Canada, and south into South America. In the south the mating season starts in December while in New Hampshire it occurs in February, although sometimes a female may not mate until early summer. The three to six young are born 63 days later. Their eyes open in about three weeks, and the mother starts to wean them when they are about two months old. The mother takes very good care of her offspring. They are generally with her, even through the first winter, despite the fact that some of the females mate when they are ten months old. The males generally wait until their second year.

Raccoons are most active after sundown when they sally forth to look for food. This consists of almost anything edible from snails, crayfish, frogs, fish to fruits, grubs, crickets, bird and turtle eggs, and even poultry. When food becomes scarce in late fall the coon goes to bed. Sometimes several families sleep together. This is not real hibernation, however, since respiration and temperature remain normal, and during mild spells in winter they come forth to look for food.

A mother coon and her young will cover from a half to one mile in their travels. Male raccoons may cover as much as five miles. Some have been trapped and tagged, later to be caught 75 miles from their original point of release.

The raccoon is a highly prized game species to many coon hunters in New Hampshire, but a pain in the neck in some localities where wood duck nesting boxes are located.

Marten

So far as red squirrels are concerned, nothing worse can happen to them than to have a marten move into their neighborhood. While marten, admittedly, eat a variety of food ranging from small mammals, birds, frogs and insects, to fruits, berries and honey, red or pine squirrels seem to be their favorite prey. Once a marten begins to chase one of these squirrels, it has little chance of escaping in tree tops. Its main hope is to find a hole too small for the enemy to enter.

The marten, closely related to its larger cousin, the fisher, is also known as pine marten or American sable. It is found in the evergreen forests of northern North America. It was once much more widespread than it is today. Its disappearance from much of northeastern United States seems to have coincided with lumbering activities when virgin pine, spruce and fir stands were cut. Then too, since these animals have a very high quality fur, trappers accounted for a great many of them. Although the marten is a secretive animal, it is also very inquisitive, to the point of being stupid. For this reason trappers have found the marten very easy to catch. There is a possibility that a few may still be found in New Hampshire.

There are approximately eleven subspecies of martens in North America. Slightly smaller than house cats, they ordinarily weigh somewhere between two and three pounds. They hunt their food both day and night. Unlike their relative, the weasel, however, they do not kill more than they need. Any surplus is buried and eaten at a later date.

Martens mate in mid-summer. The one to five young are not born until the following spring, generally in April. The nest, lined with grass and moss, is found in hollow trees or sometimes in an underground burrow. It takes a month or longer before the babies open their eyes, but, thereafter they grow so rapidly that they are practically full grown in three months. The hissing, growling, snarling and screeching animals are very playful, and extremely quick in their actions.

Fisher

If we were to select New Hampshire's fightin'est, most versatile, and most valuable furbearer, the fisher would win hands down. But why this animal is called a fisher is a mystery. Granted it will take an occasional fish, but this is the exception rather than the rule. The Chippewa Indians had a much more appropriate name. Cahalane, author of *Mammals of North America,* writes that they named the animal "tha-cho", which means big marten. It describes the animal in one sneeze.

The fisher seems to have increased in New Hampshire during the past fifteen years and has extended its range southward as far as Manchester and Hampton, if not farther. This member of the weasel family can swim, is a fast runner on the ground, and is fast enough in trees to catch squirrels and even martens. It is active both day or night, summer and winter. W. J. Hamilton, Jr. and Arthur Cook, author of *The Biology and Management of the Fisher in New York,* found that stomachs of sixty fishers killed in late fall and early winter contained deer (chiefly carrion), red squirrel, mice, shrews, hares, porcupines, birds, fruits, fern tips, and mosses. The fisher is one animal that can kill porcupines. In fact, a large fisher is even able to kill a deer. One thing in its favor is that it stores surplus food but invariably goes back to eat it. Hamilton and Cook found that fishers move in rough circuits, encompassing an area of about ten square miles. Males range more widely than do females. Of 27 males weighed, the heaviest weighed 12 pounds and 1 ounce, while of 42 females the heaviest weighed just under 7 pounds.

The breeding period is in April and the one to four blind, helpless young are born about 350 days later. This represents an unusual type of gestation called "discontinuous development" in which growth of the embryo is halted at a very early stage and is not resumed for a number of months. In fact, about a week after the young are born the mother must forsake her babies for a brief period to find a mate for one or two nights. The eyes of the young open in about seven weeks and the growing fishers begin to hunt with their mother when about three months old. The family breaks up in the late fall.

Recently members of the Fish and Game Department visited the Hudson Bay Fur Company in Montreal and asked which was considered their most valuable fur. Their answer was "the fisher".

Mink

Next to beaver the mink accounts for the highest annual gross income on New Hampshire furs. From 1950 to 1959 a total of 11,340 wild-trapped mink grossed New Hampshire trappers close to $194,000.

The mink is found throughout most of North America north of Mexico and in all of New Hampshire. This aggressive and crafty killer spends most of its time near water, establishing its home under trees along stream banks, in muskrat houses, or in natural cavities along rivers. It feeds mainly on fish, frogs, crayfish, aquatic insects, snakes, small mammals — including muskrats and birds. When on occasion one of these animals gets into a poultry pen it can be very destructive — killing a number of chickens in one night. The mink likes to eat at home, so it lugs much of its meat to its den. The remains are apt to give the nest a messy appearance.

The mink's chief enemies are large owls, bobcats, foxes, and man. When cornered or trapped this animal can go berserk with rage, twisting its face into horrible grimaces. Like skunks, the mink has two prominent anal glands which emit a powerful smelling secretion, particularly during the mating season. Fortunately, it cannot be squirted, since many people consider the smell much more obnoxious than that of a skunk.

Minks cover considerable territory in their daily search for food. The cruising range may be several square miles, the males generally roaming farther than the females.

In New Hampshire the breeding season occurs between mid-February and March. The male may have a number of affairs, but finally settles down with one female. The four to eight blind, cigarette-sized young, which are born after a gestation period of about 42 to 44 days, are weaned in approximately five weeks. Both parents bring food to the growing youngsters. These are often carried about by the scruff of the neck or may even ride on their parents' backs while swimming in the water. The young follow their parents until mid-summer, after which the family breaks up and all go their own way.

Weasel

If the weasel were the size of a bobcat, it would probably be the most dangerous animal in North America. This bloodthirsty little animal is intelligent, lightning-quick, very strong for its size, and fearless. It has been known to attack humans who have come between it and its prey. The weasel can climb trees and also swim. It follows its prey by scent, and must eat about one-third of its own weight every twenty-four hours. Its food consists mainly of mice; although frogs, chipmunks, small snakes, insects, small birds, and sometimes rabbits make up part of its diet. The weasel seems to enjoy killing, even after its appetite has been satisfied, as poultry men sometimes discover to their sorrow. Occasionally this animal runs berserk in a chicken coop, killing many dozens of chickens. Its favorite method of attack is to grab larger victims by the base of the skull, then sucking the blood and also eating the flesh.

There are three kinds in New Hampshire — the long-tailed weasel in the extreme northeastern part of the state, the New York weasel which is fairly common in the southern half of the state, and the small Bonaparte's weasel, which is common throughout the state.

Every schoolboy knows that in the north the weasel changes its coat from brown in the summer to white in the winter, the latter being sold as "ermine" by furriers. These change-overs usually take from three to five weeks.

Weasels generally live in deserted chipmunk burrows and under stumps or boulders. Their nest is usually made up of fur and feathers of their victims. Owls, hawks, cats, and large snakes are their chief enemies.

It is believed that weasels stay mated throughout the year generally. The male is considerably larger than the female. They breed early in summer. Then, as in the fisher, there is a period of several months in which the fertilized ova lie quiescent, so that the four to nine young are not born until the following April. Their eyes open about the fifth week. The male weasel assists the mother in bringing food to their offspring.

Despite its occasional forays on a poultry yard, the weasel is, as a whole, very beneficial to the farmer due to the fact that a large per cent of its food consists of small rodents such as mice and rats.

Skunk

About time of the February thaw you should become aware of skunks. In fact, if you keep your eyes and nose open, you will think they are all over the place for this is the time of year male skunks go on the prowl looking for mates. There will be a good deal of fighting and some will come out of the frays somewhat the worse for smell. About 51 days later each litter of skunks will have from four to seven blind young. After being nursed about six or seven weeks, there will come a warm June night when the mother skunk ventures forth from the den with her new offsprings, and as they follow her Indian file fashion she will introduce them to hunting. Beetles and grubs under stones, grasshoppers, garbage, mice, berries, turtle eggs, rabbits, and chicken will make up their diet.

Skunks are sociable animals. They aren't too proud to live around people, where they utilize rabbit or woodchuck holes near farms and buildings. Their dens contain nests made of dried grass and leaves where they sleep most of the day, awaking at dusk to start their nightly hunt for food. During the winter months as many as fifteen may crowd into one den to sleep right through cold spells, but sally forth during thaws.

Four kinds of skunks are found in the United States — the spotted, the hog-nosed, the hooded, and the striped. The latter is the only one found in New Hampshire. Their main enemies are the horned owl, bobcat, fox, and the automobile.

Early in life most of us become aware of the skunk's most unusual characteristic — namely, the two large glands found on each side of the anus. These are used entirely for self-defense and can be discharged one at a time or both at once. They are loaded for about five or six shots and have a range of approximately twelve feet. The skunk's aim is excellent and he does not use the tail to whip the scent about, as people erroneously believe. The skunk is usually gentleman enough to give ample warning. When he becomes excited he begins to stamp his feet, click his teeth, hiss, and even growl. All the while he looks you right in the eye. When his tail comes up, run! His favorite firing position is a U-shape, with head and rear toward the enemy.

If someone tells you a skunk is helpless when picked up by the tail, let that someone do the demonstrating while you stand at a respectful distance. Later you might tell the demonstrator that his clothes should be soaked in gasoline or ammonia.

Otter

If some budding naturalist wishes to make a contribution to our knowledge of wildlife, he can do so by finding out when the breeding season of otters occurs. This and the gestation period of otters are still wildlife mysteries. It is known that the one to five (generally two or three) young are born in April and early May, under spreading roots of trees along stream banks and in bank burrows. The young stay blind about five weeks. When they are about two months old the mother begins to teach them how to swim. At first the young generally ride around on her back. They learn their lessons well, since the grown otter is one of the best swimmers of all the land mammals. They can also swim under water about a quarter of a mile.

The young will stay with their mother about a year, leaving her shortly before the next litter is due.

Otters are very playful; playing tag, wrestling, and in particular do they enjoy tobogganing down bank slides and over ice and snow. They take a running start and then scoot along on their four paws which, turned backwards, are used like skis.

Grown otters weigh between twelve and twenty-five pounds. In the course of a year their cruising range may be as much as 50 to 100 miles of shoreline, although in any one season their travels are restricted to about three to ten miles. Their very dense and excellent fur is in considerable demand.

The otter is found throughout New Hampshire and although a definite asset to the state, this animal is not always in best standing with trout fishermen and muskrat trappers. Admittedly, an otter in a hatchery or on one of our pure trout streams or ponds is definitely persona non grata. It must also be conceded that in an area of high muskrat populations, an otter can be quite a competitor with the trapper. But his good points outweigh his bad qualities. In streams and ponds where there are rough fish, otters find it easiest to catch the slower fish. Sunfish are particularly vulnerable. Snakes, frogs, crayfish, clams, snails and an occasional bird all go to make up the rest of the otter's diet. Many people find the sight of otters in the wild of sufficient value to make up for the trout they eat.

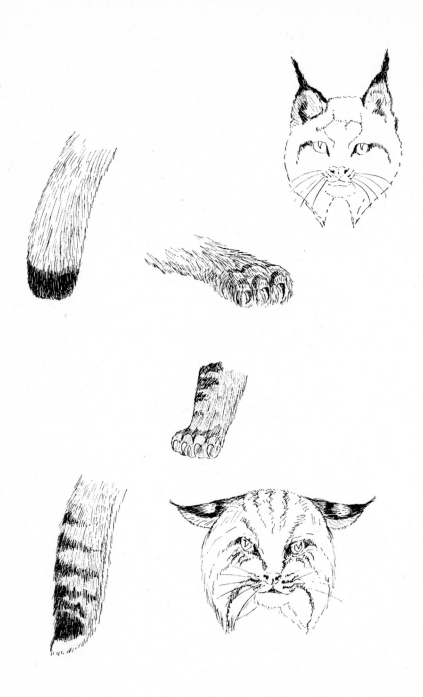

Lynx and Bobcat

Every so often we hear or read of someone killing a Canadian Lynx in New Hampshire. In most cases the animal should have been called a wildcat or bobcat. The Canada Lynx is found only in the wildest parts of New Hampshire and has become very rare. The two animals can be distinguished as follows: the lynx has large padded feet, prominent ear tufts, with a tail tipped wholly black. The common bobcat never has padded feet like the lynx; the ear tufts are less than an inch long and sometimes absent; and the tip of the tail, which is black above and white below, has three or four poorly defined brownish bars. The lynx is generally larger than the bobcat, the latter averaging about 15 or 16 pounds. While the lynx lives in remote and wild country, the bobcat has adapted itself to forests, mountains, swamps, farm land, and even the edge of cities.

The range of the bobcat is from Mexico northward through all of the United States and into southern Canada, while the lynx's range is restricted to the conifer forests of northern United States north through Canada to the northern tree limit.

The mating season of the bobcat is in February. During this time of the year they do considerable squalling and yowling, like overgrown alley cats. The gestation period is about fifty days when two to four young are born, generally in rocky ledges or in hollow logs. The young are well furred and spotted at birth, open their eyes on the ninth day, and are weaned when they are about two months old. They remain with their mother well into the summer, but by fall when they weigh about 8 to 12 pounds they are on their own.

Their food consists of snowshoe hares, squirrels, mice, muskrats, grouse, an occasional fox and porcupine, and sometimes a deer. They seem to rely more on sight than on scent when they hunt. Their range is about four to five square miles, and may cover as much as ten to fifteen square miles when food is scarce during the winter.

Both the bobcat and the lynx are shy animals and will avoid humans whenever possible. It is extremely improbable that they ever attack humans without provocation.

Seals

Recently someone found a baby seal next to the road on Odiorne Point in Rye. Since the finder wished to raise the animal he asked the New Hampshire Fish and Game Department for information about seals. We went to the books and found that knowledge about this animal is very limited.

There are six different species on the Atlantic Coast, all of them belonging to the group known as hair or earless seals as opposed to the eared seals such as the Alaska fur seal and sea-lions. The species commonly found along our New Hampshire coast and in the Great Bay is the Harbor Seal, also sometimes called the Leopard Seal because of its spotted coat. This species ranges from southern New England northward, although occasional individuals are found as far south as North Carolina.

While most species of seals are migratory, our Atlantic Harbor Seal is fairly sedentary. Since they cannot sleep in water, they come to shore or climb up on emerged objects to snooze. Seals weigh about the same as man, the male averaging about 160 pounds, while occasional individuals will reach 265 pounds. Females are generally about 25% lighter in weight. (It is doubtful that our comparison with humans will hold up, in this case!) When they are chased, seals can swim from 12 to 15 miles an hour for about half a mile and then they slow down.

Literature about the breeding habits of the Harbor Seal is scant, indeed. One book suggested that the young are born in September, which made us wonder how come the newborn pup in New Hampshire was found in May. S. A. Asdell in *Patterns of Mammalian Reproduction* states that on the Pacific Coast the young are born over a period of three to four months, beginning in May, and that mating generally occurs in September. This is probably also applicable to ours on the Atlantic Coast.

As a rule seals give birth to one pup, sometimes two. These are covered with a white fetal coat which is exchanged for a spotted one a few days after birth. The young weigh between 25 and 30 pounds when born, and they are nursed for about four to six weeks.

Seals are intelligent and inquisitive creatures and apt to be very friendly when not molested.

Wild Boar

Unless other states have been successful with recent introductions, New Hampshire, Tennessee and North Carolina have the doubtful honor of being the only states in the United States which now have huntable populations of European Boar roaming their forests. This wary game animal is located mainly in the towns of Croydon, Plainfield, Grantham, and Cornish in Western New Hampshire and in the Cherokee National Forest in Southeastern Tennessee. Those in Tennessee are the result of boars brought from Germany in 1912 and liberated within the enclosures of a hunting club near Hooper Bald in North Carolina, while those in New Hampshire were brought from the Black Forest in Germany in the early 1890's, and some later from Russia, and planted in Corbin's Park in Sullivan County.

These animals should not be confused with domestic hogs gone wild, often referred to as "Piney Woods Rooters" in southern states, or with the peccary (or javelina hog), a wild pig found in southwestern United States and Central and South America. The peccary is a comparatively small pig with adults ranging in weight somewhere between 40 and 65 pounds. The European wild boar, on the other hand, is a large powerful animal reaching a height of over three feet and weight of 400 pounds. Specimens have been taken in Germany weighing over 600 pounds. A 304½ pound boar is the largest specimen known to have been taken in New Hampshire.

A characteristic of the peccary is the strong, musky odor it leaves along its trails. This scent comes from a gland which is located on the pig's back about eight inches in front of its tiny tail. It is so pronounced that humans can easily smell it.

The European Boar differs from domestic pigs in several respects. The wild boar has a high erect mane on the upper part of the neck and spine, which makes the shoulders appear higher than the hips. The head is long, ending in a slender snout. The tail is long and mule-like with a tuft of long hair at the tip. Canine teeth are well developed in both sexes, and in males become large, upwardly directed tusks. (The canines of the peccary are straight and grow in a vertical direction.)

It is believed that wild boars reach sexual maturity at 1½ years. Large wild boars will often visit tame sows and breed, driving off or killing the tame boars. This has occurred on various occasions in Tennessee where there are now numerous semi-wild domestic pigs. The rutting season for these boars in New Hampshire has not been established. It probably occurs sometime from the latter part of November through December to January, as it does in Germany. The gestation period is somewhere between 18 and 20 weeks and there is probably but one litter of from 3 to 7 young. When the sow is ready to give birth she seeks a secluded spot in a soft well-concealed bed. The young do not leave the bed for the first few days. When born they resemble a chipmunk, being about 6 inches long, and having rust or sandy colored longitudinal stripes which disappear about the sixth month.

Our native American pig, the peccary, on the other hand selects a hollow log or a burrow in which to have her young. The babies, generally twins, may be born through at least six months of the year. At birth the reddish brown young have a black stripe running down the center of their back. They are able to walk the first day of birth and within several days, with their mother, they join other males and females to form a band — often 25 or more — rooting around during the day after food.

Wild boars, too, often band together doing most of their feeding at night. They shift from area to area depending on their food supply, which consists of a wide variety of items ranging from berries to nuts and roots to carrion. Due to their alertness and nervousness they are a first rate game animal, but their occasional invasion of agricultural crops can make them a pest.

White-Tailed Deer

The white-tailed deer is the most important big game animal on the North American continent. It played a vital role in the days of the early settler when it served as a principle source of meat. In fact, venison was more important than beef. The tallow was used for soap and candles, and hides were made into breeches, jackets, and moccasins. Today, this mammal entices millions of Americans into the forests and woodlots of our country each autumn. The money spent by these hunters has become an important source of revenue to many types of business.

There are three major groupings of deer in North America: the black-tailed deer, the mule deer, and the white-tail. Each shows variations from one region to another. No less than thirty subspecies of white-tails have been described, being found throughout the length and breadth of our country, and from the latitude of the Hudson Bay in Canada south to the Isthmus of Panama. These subspecies vary considerably in size, the larger generally found in the north and the smaller in the south. The largest of them all is perhaps the Northern Woodland White-tailed Deer found in New England.

There are several unusual features about deer, not the least of these being the annual development of antlers by the males. During the first autumn of life, antler development consists of barely discernible "buttons"; the following year it can be anywhere from a spike to a set of antlers; and thereafter, if food conditions are good, full sets of antlers with varying numbers of points are developed. Size of the adults' antlers depends in the main on food conditions and not on age. Sometime during August antlers on most bucks have reached full growth. At this time they are said to be in "velvet" because the antlers are covered with a velvet-like growth of skin. During August and September this skin begins to dry and peel. The buck helps this process along by rubbing the antlers against small trees. About this time he begins to "shadow fight" with sapling trees. As the rutting season approaches his neck starts to swell. Some males establish territories during the pre-breeding season and if another buck comes in the vicinity they paw the earth and thrash brush and at times battles occur.

It is often said that the most dangerous animal in the United States is a pet buck deer. This statement has a good deal of truth to it, simply because the average person who keeps a pet deer cannot apprehend what a psychological transformation this pet undergoes in autumn. As the rutting season approaches and the velvet has been rubbed off the antlers, the buck has a deadly weapon on its head. No matter how tame and affectionate he was during the summer months, he now becomes pugnacious, occasionally to the extent that he becomes half-crazed.

The peak breeding season in New Hampshire is generally around November 20. Our hunting season takes advantage of the fact that bucks lose their usual caution during this time when they are pursuing does; consequently, although sportsmen are permitted to harvest both does and bucks in New Hampshire, more bucks are annually taken than does. During this time male deer begin to lose weight. Studies have shown that bucks 3½ years and older, averaging about 192 pounds in New Hampshire on November 1, will lose 24% of their weight in nine weeks. Does do not show this decided drop. Toward the end of December and through January the bucks lose their antlers. These seem to be very attractive to all types of rodents, which soon devour them. Not until April or May does new antler growth begin.

With loss of antlers the buck's aggressiveness also disappears. Thereafter, deer of both sexes and all ages do not hesitate to group together if necessary. This happens in mid-winter, particularly in northern New Hampshire where deer "yard up" in protected areas, staying there until snow begins to melt. As anyone can see, while deer are concentrated in small areas there will be competition for food. When a longer than normal winter occurs with greater than average snow depths, food conditions can often become acute. At such times many deer may starve to death. Their food consists of tips and buds of shrubs and various hardwoods. As winter progresses these are browsed and deer are progressively forced to feed on less palatable and nutritious food, often finally finding it necessary to utilize the bark of conifers. It is for this reason that New Hampshire advocates a long hunting season, to keep the deer herd thinned down.

Many sportsmen are amazed by the fact that New Hampshire's deer herd continues to thrive despite a long hunting season and the shooting of both sexes. The ability of deer to stand up under this heavy harvest can be attributed mainly to two factors: ideal habitat and their high reproductive capacity. After a gestation period of around 201 days, from one to four fawns are born (in New Hampshire an average of 1.8 fawns per adult doe). At birth the male fawns weigh an average of about 7½ pounds while the females average about 5½ pounds. By the time they are approximately twelve hours old they are able to nurse standing. One of the first instincts they exhibit is to drop instantly when frightened. There is considerable evidence that fawns have no scent the first few days.

During the first three months fawns are covered with 250 to 350 white spots. Although they begin to forage on grass tips and browse when they are two or three weeks old, they are not weaned until they are nearly four months old.

When deer are observed during the summer months they are generally found in family groups consisting of the doe and her fawns, occasionally accompanied by the previous year's offspring. In the meantime, the bucks, who are in the process of developing sensitive antlers, prefer to be alone. Around August the adult deer begin to shed their reddish coat to be gradually replaced by heavier and longer bluish-grey hairs which serve as their winter coat.

The age of deer can be determined by their teeth. In the wild, deer seldom live over ten years. Penned deer, on the other hand, have been known to reach the age of nineteen years.

Did you know that deer do not have a gall bladder; that they are very much afraid of snakes?

A recent publication put out by the Wildlife Management Institute, entitled *The Deer of North America,* has summarized under one cover the sum total of knowledge concerning this mammal.

To most people deer are deer. It is only after intimate contact with these animals that we occasionally discover that each animal has a personality of its own. Mrs. Helenette Silver, who was asked to raise eight fawns in preparation for our nutrition studies, made this discovery. Some of her observations follow, to demonstrate how varied the personalities of growing fawns can be.

"Like all species, deer have certain common behavior patterns. Nervous and suspicious by nature, they are nevertheless affectionate and enjoy human company once you have gained their confidence. Among themselves they are sociable and friendly. Although the bucks fight furiously during the rut, and are dangerous at this time, ordinarily they are peaceful . . . .

"While deer do not attack, they will sometimes turn on humans if cornered or threatened. They can never be disciplined — either they will panic, dashing blindly into fences, walls or other obstacles, or they will fight back, possibly injuring the handler. Like royalty they demand the services and degree of familiarity they require and intend to tolerate. Any time a deer does what you want it to, you can be sure this coincides with its own desires. All deer are not, however, cut from the same cloth. Superimposed on the common behavior patterns are individual personalities just as distinct as among humans. These, even more than differences in physique, enable us to tell them apart as easily as you recognize members of your family . . . .

"Some interesting variations were displayed among eight fawns raised this summer. They were evenly divided as to sex — four bucks and four does. *Baldy* was a good three weeks old when received. At this age fawns usually become quite wild and are much harder to tame than younger ones. Baldy was, however, self-confident and friendly — almost bold. He was not especially dependent until weaning time, when he suddenly became a regular mother's boy, obliging us to keep him on a bottle several weeks longer than any of the others. He finally condescended to drink if I would hold the pan, but he slowed his rate of gain through neglecting his grain to follow me about as I did the chores. He still permits the other deer to eat his portion if I will pet him. He is quite timid with strangers . . . .

"*Wildroot* (Wildroot Creamoil Charlie on account of his immaculate grooming) is a beautiful, tractable, polite fellow. Very tame but not maudlin in his affection, he is also very determined and effective in getting his own way — the executive type. When only about a month old he utilized a very human device, amounting to a mild form of delinquency, to gain attention. Wildroot, being co-operative, was naturally always fed last. After about a week he took to retiring to a corner when his turn came; obviously wanting to eat, he also wanted to be teased. On being urged, he ate well. When this did not gain him as much attention as he wanted, he adopted stronger measures. He was tame enough when we entered the pen, but refused to eat even when coaxed, and dashed about in what seemed to be blind terror when it came his turn to feed. He was left twenty-four hours without food to get over his nonsense, to no avail. After a second day without food he was offered the first bottle, which he accepted like a cosset lamb. He never repeated his bad-boy act, nor was it necessary to give him precedence at every feeding. He just didn't want to be always the neglected one . . . .

"*Halftrack* was run over by a mowing machine, necessitating the amputation at the hairline of one section of his left hind hoof. Because of this injury he was handled less than any of the other fawns. Visits to the veterinary for dressing were not pleasant, and he was wild and untouchable, and would not nurse from a bottle. After a great deal of special attention he permits me to pet him when no one is about, and will leave the barn at feeding time if I will follow him out into the pasture with an individual handout. He is an introvert; stays by himself, sleeps alone, and does not conform to the regular schedule of feeding and play unless rounded up in the pasture. He is no longer particularly timid but bows to no authority, is very alert, and has the makings of a wild deer. He has no friends among his own kind, and no attachment for humans other than myself is apparent . . . .

"*Pert,* largest of the does, was born on the farm, of a tame doe. Accustomed to humans from the moment of her birth, she has never been wild and is more like a domestic animal. She was taken from her mother when three weeks old, and preferred to drink from a pan. She is large-boned, a little swaybacked, placid and dependable — not handsome or brilliant, or glamorous, but you can count on her in an emergency to set an example for the more flighty — the backbone-of-society, salt-of-the-earth type of female . . . .

"*Alvin* is a moron. He has always had a very narrow head, which he carried low, neck extended and swinging from side to side in the manner of some hunting carnivores. He was slow and clumsy; he never played, and frequently fell down if he tried to hurry. In a dash for the trough he was as likely to land in it face down as on his feet. At first he did not even know how to nurse properly and would try to suck fence wires or swallow the bottle, bottom first. His appetite was ravenous and anything he could get into his mouth — rocks, filth, paper — was grist for his mill. He habitually overate and suffered from bloat and chronic diarrhea. He was treated with every known type of vitamins and mineral supplement, but nothing changed him. Tests for parasites were negative. He was too stupid to be afraid, and was the tamest of all the fawns. Visitors felt especially drawn to this poor little waif who would

poke pathetically out of the bushes and tug at their pant legs or skirts while all the other deer remained hidden. There was nothing personal, however, in Alvin's devotion to the human race; anything or anybody he could sink his teeth into was for him. He has begun to grow, and there is no longer anything abnormal about his appetite except its size. He will never be bright, but with intensive training he may become a self-supporting member of his community . . . .

"*Grey Lady* had been chased by dogs when we got her. She was exhausted and, although her injuries were superficial, her head was almost entirely skinned. She was so weak that we just fed her and let her lead her own quiet life without much hope that we could get her through. In August she began to grow and her face, which had been bare all summer, haired out with its winter coat. She was the first to shed her spots and has overtaken and passed the four smaller fawns in size. She has an unusually broad forehead and is very intelligent. Quiet and rather shy, she can now be petted and will eat from our hands . . . .

"*Sprite* is the essence of femininity. Until they start their antler buds it is almost impossible to tell the bucks from the does, but no one would ever mistake Sprite for a buck. She is exceptionally beautiful, graceful and affectionate — and something of an exhibitionist. She is the glamor girl who poses for all the camera adicts who visit the deer. When received she was very small and in poor condition, and later had enteritis. Nevertheless, she has made a better rate of growth than any of the others — possibly because of her close relationship and complete trust in us. She and Miss Muffett are chums, but Sprite is definitely the leader. When the deer escaped, Sprite twice rounded up Muffett and brought her to us before the less intelligent Muffett could be captured . . . .

"If *Miss Muffett* were human she would have stringy, mouse-colored hair and buck teeth, and wear glasses. Originally even smaller than Sprite, she has never caught up with the other fawns. She tries hard to please, but never comes up with anything original or interesting. Her personality is completely colorless and her mentality and physical attractions are equally limited, although she is now in good condition. It is difficult to feel really attracted to her. Not obviously retarded like Alvin, she is just a wallflower."

These observations could have had an interesting conclusion if the deer, in turn, could have recorded their opinions of people.

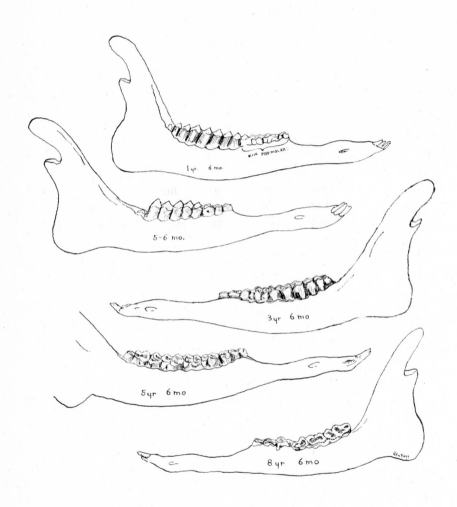

1 yr   6 mo.

MILK PREMOLAR

5-6 mo.

3 yr   6 mo

5 yr   6 mo

8 yr   6 mo

Ageing Deer

There is but one accurate method of determining the age of a deer, and that is by examining the teeth. The size of a deer, the number of points on a buck's antlers, or grayness of the face can be very misleading indicators. After some practice, however, a man can tell the age of a deer with a considerable degree of accuracy up to its sixth year, by examining the teeth.

Although sketches of jaw bones and considerably more detail than is here advisable would be necessary to point out the fine points of difference commonly used by biologists to "age deer", Game Biologist Henry Laramie will make an attempt to point out some of the major differences.

To start with, it is advisable first of all to cut open the cheek of the deer from the corner of the mouth back almost to the ear. Open the mouth as wide as possible to expose the grinding surfaces of the teeth. An examination of the jaws will show that deer do not have teeth in the front of the mouth on the upper jaw, but that there are six molars on each side of the back of the jaw bone. It is the lower set of molars which is commonly used to determine the age.

First of all, count the number of points on the teeth. If there are less than ten and all but the first two are very sharp, the deer is a fawn.

If there are ten or more points, the deer is 1½ years or older. If all the teeth are very sharp and show little wear, the deer is less than 3½ years old. It should be pointed out, however, that the first three molars (the pre-molars) are replaced at about eighteen months of age. Just before being replaced, the baby teeth will show considerable wear. If the teeth show a definite rounding of the points, the deer is between 3½ years and 5½ years old; and if the teeth are worn into a shallow cup, the deer is 5½ years or older. A very old deer will often have the teeth worn right down to the gums.

Deer's Weight

Many a hunter has wondered how much his deer weighed when it was alive. A graph is herewith reproduced from MASSACHU-SETTS WILDLIFE which should help settle many an argument. It is assumed, of course, that the weights of deer are reasonably similar in northeastern states where both bucks and does are hunted.

Example: Your deer weighs 110 lbs. dressed (internal organs including heart, liver, and lungs removed). Find this point on the left-hand vertical scale. Follow the 110 line across until you hit the slanted line. At this point follow the line down until you hit the horizontal scale. Your deer weighed 140 lbs.

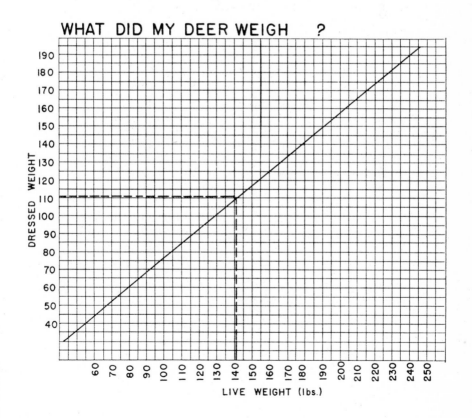

Elk

Since the New Hampshire Fish and Game Department found it necessary to reduce the state's elk herd to diminish crop damage, many queries have been received concerning this animal.

Zoologists are not happy about the name "elk" given this animal, believing the name "wapiti" would be more correct since it is closely related to the Asiatic wapitis. When the white man first arrived on this continent elk were widely distributed throughout much of the United States. Although there are no written records of them being found in New England, an elk antler was found in a lime deposit from Lyme Pond in Columbia, indicating that they may once have been present here.

The current herd is found in several towns in Sullivan County, having spread there from an original stocking of elk in Corbin's Park, Croydon. There are six forms of elk in America. Although not certain, Helen Silver, the Department's research clerk, believes that the Corbin's Park herd came from Minnesota, making the species presently found in New Hampshire the Eastern Elk.

Olaus J. Murie, author of *The Elk of North America,* stated that the average weight of certain forms of western elk is 600 pounds, with records of bull elk having been shot weighing 1100 pounds. Adult elk will, as a rule, have a set of antlers with six points. A record antler reported by Murie was from a Rocky Mountain Elk with a beam length of 64¾ inches, and one with a spread of 74 inches. Antlers are generally shed in February and March. The velvet from newly grown antlers is then shed in August and September, shortly after which the rutting season starts. During rutting the bulls like to create wallows in damp ground and roll in them; they "bugle" a high-pitched noise which rings through the forests, and do some fighting — which is less vicious than that of deer. Their main concern seems to be to round up all the cow elks they can and maintain them as a herd, while less fortunate bulls try to steal as many members of these harems as possible. Gestation is about 249 to 262 days, the single young (rarely twins) being born in late May.

Since there has been considerable discussion among sportsmen as to the desirability of having elk in New Hampshire, we herewith list some of the possible assets and liabilities.

First of all, there are many who consider elk meat superior in taste to that of most other wild game and considerably tastier than venison. Add to this the large size of the elk, and the man who brings one home will make quite an inroad on his grocery bill. Another factor in favor of the elk is that its numbers are fairly easy to control. The ever-present danger of overpopulation so difficult to control in deer is negligible in elk for two reasons. One, elk have a much lower reproductive capacity than deer. Where a female deer will often breed when six months old, cow elks breed for the first time in their third year and then usually give birth to but one young — sometimes twins. Secondly, even when elk become too numerous in a locality it is fairly simple to reduce the herd to any number desired — even extermination — because of a peculiar habit elk have in autumn of panicking when shot at and milling about in a herd. This habit is also considered one of the elk's major liabilities as a game species, since slaughtering a herd of milling animals might appeal to the meat hunter but not to a true sportsman.

There are, however, more serious liabilities to consider when introducing elk into a region. An ordinary cattle fence is no obstacle to elk when they are on the move. Since they jump no higher than necessary, they are apt to break fences when going over. Damage by elk to agriculture could thus be difficult to control.

Elk feed on pretty much the same foods as deer. This can be serious in areas of deep snow where deer are forced to yard up. Since elk can reach higher than deer, they could soon starve out a herd of deer should they happen to choose the same yarding area.

The most serious problem involving elk is their susceptibility to diseases, some of which are infectious to domestic livestock. Most common is necrotic stomatitis, which is generally fatal. Scabies is also common in elk and so is arthritis. Of most concern to cattlemen is the fact that elk harbor Bang's disease. In fact, it is so common among elk in western states that Olaus J. Murie, who wrote *The Elk of North America,* believes this to be a major factor in the low reproductive capacity of this animal. He indicates that only about one-third of mature cow elks give birth to young.

Moose

Like lumberjacks seeing the bright lights after a long winter's logging operation, so in recent years have bull moose taken to visiting New Hampshire cities in autumn. Berlin, Laconia, Manchester, and even the southern gateway to the Granite State — Nashua; the moose has paid his respects to all. The question is, "What for?"

The moose is by nature an individualist who prefers the solitudes of northern coniferous forests. There was a time, several hundred years ago, when he was more common in northern New Hampshire than our white-tailed deer. Early New Hampshire histories frequently allude to the many moose. One Nathan Caswell was credited with killing ninety-nine in one winter. As the white man moved in and increased, the moose gradually decreased and moved out. Today there are probably no more than forty or fifty in the whole state.

Perhaps it is this scarcity of mates which annually causes individual males to visit the farthest corners of the state. This explanation seems most logical since these tours generally take place in September and October during the moose's rutting season.

Are moose dangerous? Even this question has no certain answer. Peterson, recent author of *North American Moose* writes: "Every fall one reads of dozens of cases of people being attacked 'within an inch of their lives' yet hardly anyone seems to get killed or even hurt." If ever a moose had reason to be potentially dangerous, it was the one in Penacook (October 1955) as he was chased through back yards by dogs, children, and photographers, while mothers screamed from porches. But everyone had a good time, perhaps even the moose. On the other hand, there are authentic records of moose charging cars and making considerable alterations to the body.

This largest member of the deer family consists of seven subspecies. These encircle the North Pole, being restricted to the evergreen forests.

To better understand the problems of the moose in New Hampshire, it is well to know a little about its life history.

The rutting season generally occurs between September 15 and October 15, at which time the bull may do considerable roaming.

An interesting habit of mating moose is their tendency to make wallows in which they roll to cover themselves with mud. The gestation period is normally between 240 and 246 days. Moose usually give birth to a single calf, occasionally to twins, and rarely to triplets. Many cows are barren. Randolph L. Peterson, author of *North American Moose,* estimates that less than half the cows produce calves each year and that a high percentage fail to produce offspring before their third year.

The calves are born the latter part of May or early June. They are dark reddish-brown at birth with a dark stripe down their back, and weigh between 15 and 35 pounds. The newborn calf is very tame and can easily be caught. After it is several days old, however, it can outrun a man. At this period of its life it has a high pitched voice, almost like that of a human. The greatest mortality to the little ones is due to drowning and, perhaps, to bear.

Even the newly born calf has the "bell" or dewlap (a growth on the throat) which is characteristic of moose. The antler growth of the young male calf may consist of small "buttons" during the first year. At about one year of age he has his first set of spikes, which are sometimes forked. Two-year old bulls generally have branched antlers and in succeeding years these begin to show palmation or flattening, reaching their maximum growth after the sixth year. The antlers usually reach full development in August and September when the velvet is rubbed off. Two-year olds shed antlers in April and each year thereafter the antlers are shed a little earlier until the moose reaches the prime of its life, when shedding occurs in December. Maximum age is probably about twenty years. The hearing and sense of smell of moose are highly efficient, while their sight is such that an optometrist would pre-scribe glasses. They are powerful swimmers and will dive after food completely below the water's surface. They eat from 40 to 60 pounds of food daily.

Diseases and Parasites of Mammals

Every year New Hampshire sportsmen bring some kind of game or furbearer to the Fish and Game Department and ask: "What was the matter with this animal?" Although the Department biologists are not, as a rule, trained to be pathologists (disease specialists), most of them have had enough contact with diseased specimens of wildlife to enable them to recognize some of the more commonplace cases.

When a man brings in a sick mink, for instance, we will invariably examine that mink's kidneys first. Here in New Hampshire the kidney worm seems to be quite common. This is one of the largest of the round worms. A mink recently examined by us had a worm over a foot in length which had completely destroyed one kidney, leaving nothing but a hollow shell. It is as a leech-like animal when found on crayfish; and certain species of fish are known to be intermediary hosts to this worm.

From time to time trappers will also find fairly small round worms embedded in the musculature of the mink's feet or legs. This worm, commonly known as the Guinea Worm, has also been found in the hind feet of raccoons.

Several years ago the raccoons of our state went through quite an epidemic. Infected individuals seemed to lose their fear of humans. Quite often they would sit or lie on the ground shivering. Distemper, jaundice, and a new virus disease were all suspected; the true cause is still a mystery.

Deer are surprisingly healthy animals. Occasionally, however, a hunter will shoot one that has skin tumors. Sometimes these unsightly black or gray "warts" are as big as a basketball and can be found on nearly any part of the body. Deer have been brought into the laboratory with tumors completely covering the head and face of the animal. At times the successful deer hunter is quite disconcerted to find what looks like blood suckers in the liver of his deer. These liver flukes are also found in cattle. Eggs from these flukes pass out of the host animal and hatch in water where the microscopic larvae seek suitable water snails in which to develop. After a period of time, tadpole-like forms develop in the snail, pass out, and come to rest on water plants. If a deer or cow happens to eat one of these plants, presto, flukes in the liver.

172

Since bear hunting is becoming increasingly popular in New Hampshire, a word of warning is in order. Bear meat should be thoroughly cooked before it is eaten. Like pigs, bear can harbor the deadly trichinosis.

Sportsmen in our state became much aware of mange several years ago when this affliction decimated our red fox population. This skin disease seems to be related to the number of foxes — the more foxes the more mange there is. Mange is caused by tiny mites which get into the skin and become very irritating to the infected animal. The constant irritation produces a flow of serum and blood which forms large scabs on the body, sometimes to the extent that foxes are left practically hairless and in a very weakened condition. The epidemic of mange in New Hampshire seems to have somewhat subsided, after it helped thin out the fox population.

In discussing fox disease in New Hampshire we are very fortunate not to have to include rabies. Although various foxes have been brought to us that appeared rabid, to date they have always proved negative. One reason for this may be that gray foxes are more susceptible than red foxes, and this species is fairly uncommon in New Hampshire. Our state should, however, keep constant vigil in regard to this disease and take extremely vigorous and drastic measures to counteract its spread the first time a rabid fox is reported.

Many rabbits have been brought into our laboratory because their livers had white spots. Sportsmen have become very tularemia conscious and know that white spots on the liver is one of the symptoms. However, in all cases so far these white spots have not been the tiny whitish pinhead-sized spots of tularemia but larger, pencil eraser-sized glistening spots caused by the larvae of the dog tapeworm. These spots and trails can also be found on the intestines. They do not affect the meat once the insides have been removed, but don't let your dog eat the entrails of such a rabbit.

Occasionally hunters report finding a grub in the skin of the rabbit, generally around the neck. This is the larva of a bot fly, taking a free ride until ready to emerge as a fly. It does not affect the meat of the rabbit. So far we know of no instance of tularemia in New Hampshire rabbits.

Rabies

In recent years much has been heard about rabies. A serious outbreak starting in New York State about 1945, first in dogs and then in foxes, made residents of New Hampshire more aware of this deadly disease. To date we have no authentic record of a case in our state since 1945. Many people are probably unaware that there has been some very fine teamwork behind the scenes between conservation officers, biologists, and the Board of Health watching for possible outbreaks. Conservation officers have brought quite a few suspicious acting foxes and racoons into the Fish and Game Laboratory to be checked for rabies. Here biologists prepare the specimen for examination by severing the head from the body, and then it is delivered to the Diagnostic Laboratories in the State Hospital. In every case to date, these specimens have proved negative.

Rabies occurs throughout the year and is not confined to the summer hot spells called "dog days", as some believe. All warm-blooded animals, including poultry, can get the disease. A human becomes infected only when the rabies virus enters an open wound so it can make contact with nerve tissue. The virus makes its way from the nerve tissue into the mouth of infected animals through the salivary glands. That is why the bite of a rabid animal is so dangerous.

Rabies occur in two forms, furious and dumb, although the disease is the same. Animals affected by the vicious type are nervous and excitable in the early stages and will shy at the slightest noise. They wander many miles and at times will attack any man or animal who crosses their path. If they do not die in a fit in this stage, they always pass into the dumb stage before death. In this stage they do not wander from home or attack other animals. Paralysis sets in early and within two or three days increases to such a degree that the animal falls into a coma and dies. Animals suffering from rabies are without fear. Anyone bitten by a wild animal whose actions seem fearless should attempt, if at all possible, to capture the animal and keep it locked up alive to make determination of the disease easier. Always report to a doctor.

The sportsman can help by not permitting species such as foxes and raccoons to become overpopulated, and by reporting suspicious acting animals to a conservation officer.

AMPHIBIANS AND REPTILES

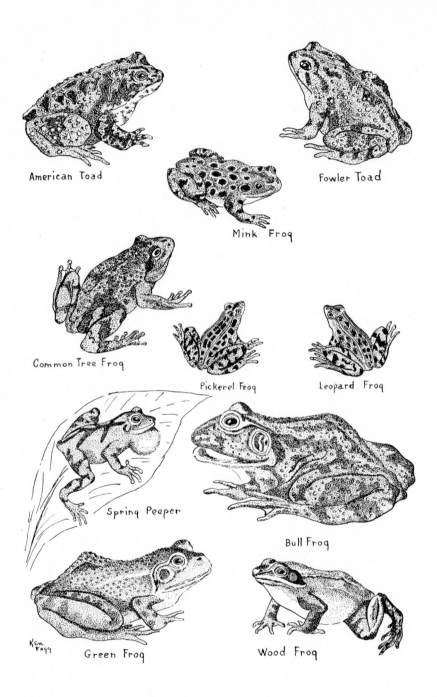

American Toad

Fowler Toad

Mink Frog

Common Tree Frog

Pickerel Frog

Leopard Frog

Spring Peeper

Bull Frog

Ken Fogg

Green Frog

Wood Frog

Toads and Frogs in New Hampshire

It is difficult to stroll too far afield in New Hampshire at dusk in spring without wondering how the vast multitude of toads and frogs heard all about us can be so hidden from view during the daytime. Early settlers who first came to America from Europe wrote glowing accounts of the music by frogs. One Irishman hearing frogs peeping for the first time remarked: "Begorrah, but they stop out of tune to a nicety".

Although there are almost a hundred different kinds of toads and frogs in the United States and Canada, only ten are found in New Hampshire. They are the American Toad, Fowler's Toad, Common Tree-Toad or Frog, Spring Peeper, Eastern Wood Frog, Leopard Frog, Pickerel Frog, Green Frog, Mink Frog, and Bullfrog. It's the spring Peepers (one of the Tree Frogs) with their shrill, clear, high pitched notes we hear above all others soon after ice goes out. While they hold down the soprano, the wood frog clacks the bass, sounding almost like the quack of a duck. Later the American Toad starts to chime in with its long drawn-out, melodious trill. Although males do the singing, the females are not voiceless.

The number of eggs laid varies for the different species, with some laying as few as six eggs while the Bullfrog lays as many as 20,000. Some lay single eggs, some twos, and some in small packets. Other species produce bead-like strings, or bands, while some lay them in balls and lumps. The eggs of some species float while those of others sink. In the North the breeding season for each species lasts about four to five weeks, with the exception of the American Toad and Green Frog who need from two to three months. Eggs hatch in three to twenty days, depending on temperatures and other conditions.

Anyone interested in these extremely interesting creatures should own *Handbook of Frogs and Toads* by Wright and Wright, and supplement his reading material with a set of records entitled *Voices of the Night* on which the Albert R. Brand Bird Song Foundation of Cornell University has recorded the calls of 26 frogs and toads found in eastern North America.

American Toad

One of the most useful animals around the house, but often least appreciated, is the American Toad. The home range of this unobtrusive little creature seldom exceeds a quarter of an acre, where it spends a great part of time feeding on insects, millipedes, sowbugs, snails, and earthworms. On hot days it may dig a hole in soft soil and back into it or crawl under a board, stone, or other object, coming out in the evening to look for food. There are still people who harbor the silly but untrue superstition that one must not touch toads because "they give warts".

With the coming of heavy frosts, toads go into hibernation and stay there until the snow melts. Soon after they emerge from their winter's sleep and when ice has melted in the ponds, toads leave their home grounds to start mass migrations to nearby open water to breed. This generally starts in April in northern United States and may continue into the early part of the summer. It is at this time of the year one can hear their long, drawn-out melodious trilling. A female can lay between 4,000 and 8,000 eggs. These are deposited in two strings, in long spiral tubes of jelly; and it takes these from 3 to 12 days to incubate. It takes the small (a little over one inch) black tadpoles about 50 to 65 days to transform into toads. Then starts a big migration away from their birthplace. At such times it will often seem as if the ground is alive with tiny toads. It takes them from one to two years to reach maturity.

It is not known what the average life expectancy of the American Toad is in the wild. There is a record of one that lived to be 31 years old.

There are at least 21 different kinds of toads in the United States and Canada. The American Toad ranges from Minnesota and Oklahoma east to the Atlantic Coast, and from northern Georgia and Virginia north as far as latitude 50 degrees in Canada from Manitoba across to Gaspe.

Salamanders in New Hampshire

Most of us have undoubtedly seen many salamanders in New Hampshire. Still, there is perhaps no form of wildlife in the state about which we know less. Some people call salamanders lizards. There are no lizards in New Hampshire. Lizards have scales while salamanders do not. Salamanders in our state are perfectly harmless. They are generally secretive and most active at night.

Although there are 126 known kinds of salamanders in the United States and Canada, only nine species have been found in New Hampshire. The largest of these is the purple salamander, which reaches a length of between 5½ and 7 inches, while the smallest is the four-toed salamander which averages 2½ inches in length. The most common is the dusky salamander, while the rarest in New Hampshire is probably the marbled salamander, only known to be collected from around Milford. Most of them hibernate during winter. They do not sing, such as do frogs, but some can click, squeak, or bleat.

Breeding activities vary with different species. Some mate in spring and some in fall, and some go through very interesting courtship activities. Individuals of the common spotted salamander, for instance, will generally congregate in large groups in early spring to indulge in a kind of a nuptial dance, swimming about vigorously, rubbing and nosing one another until the water fairly boils.

Eggs may be laid singly or in masses from a few to several hundred and take from about twenty to sixty days to hatch, each species demonstrating individual differences. The females of the marbled, the four-toed, the dusky, and the gray-backed salamanders stay with their eggs until they hatch. The latter lays its eggs in hollows of well-rotted logs, suspending the eggs in the hollow like a cluster of grapes.

As a whole, salamanders live on worms, insects, small crustaceans and molluscs. Some are quite beautiful. One of the prettiest is the orange-red salamander often found under logs or in cool, damp places. This is the immature eft of the red-spotted newt. Anyone interested in these little-known animals will do well to obtain *Handbook of Salamanders* by Sherman C. Bishop.

Black Snake

DeKay's Snake

Ring-necked Snake

Garter Snake

Smooth Green Snake

Red-bellied Snake

Spotted Adder

Ribbon Snake

Banded Water Snake

Spreading Adder

Timber Rattlesnake

Snakes in New Hampshire

There are two kind of reptiles native to New Hampshire — snakes and turtles.

There are eleven species of snakes in the state, of which only one can be considered a liability — the rattlesnake. The good that the other ten species perform in feeding on rodents, insects, and rough fish, and by being used as food by other predators far outweighs the little damage committed by the one outlaw.

With the exception of Maine there is perhaps no other state in the United States so free of poisonous snakes as New Hampshire. Professor H. D. Carle of Keene Teachers College, an authority on the snakes of New Hampshire, states that rattlesnakes are currently found in only three restricted areas of the state: Wintastiquet Mountain in Hinsdale and Chesterfield, a deserted granite quarry in Allenstown from where they spread to Hooksett during the summer, and near Dan Hole Pond in Tuftonboro. The N. H. Bureau of Vital Statistics reports no fatalities from snakes in this state in recent years.

The rattlesnake develops new fangs about every three months, generally swallowing the old ones as they become embedded in the snake's prey. It sheds its skin approximately three times a summer, each time adding a new ring to its rattle. A snake can strike a maximum distance of about two-thirds its body length, although seldom striking more than half that distance.

In New Hampshire five species of snakes reproduce by laying eggs — the black snake, green snake, ring-neck snake, spotted adder, and spreading adder. The other six species retain the eggs within their body until they hatch and then give birth to young ones. The common garter snake may give birth to as many as fifty young ones, generally in August, while the little ring-necked snake produces only about one to six eggs, generally in July.

The black snake is the largest snake in the state, but seldom reaches a length of six feet. The average length of our smallest snake, the red-bellied snake, is about ten inches. At birth its young can be curled up on a dime.

Turtles in New Hampshire

Of the approximately 260 kinds of known turtles, only seven are found in New Hampshire: musk, snapping, spotted, wood, Blanding's, box, and painted turtles. These reptiles generally require warm climates and consequently few are found as far north as southern Canada.

The most common turtle in this state is the colorful painted turtle, found in most ponds of southern New Hampshire. The wood turtle is perhaps second in abundance. Blanding's turtles and box turtles are so rare in New Hampshire that the Research Division would appreciate having any found in this state.

New Hampshire's smallest turtle is the little "stink pot" or musk turtle, while the largest is the snapping turtle which in this state sometimes reaches a weight of forty pounds. Turtles are usually long-lived. Clifford Pope, author of *Turtles of the United States and Canada*, reports there is an authentic record of a tortoise on Mouritius which was known to have lived 152 years, and perhaps quite some longer, that met an untimely death through an accident.

Turtles generally mate in spring, laying their eggs in June and July. These usually hatch in September. However, some turtles mate in September and some eggs do not hatch until the following spring. The eggs are usually laid and buried in a flask-shaped hole in the ground which the turtle digs with its hind feet. Land turtles lay relatively few eggs. Some of the smaller ones lay from two to six eggs, while some of the larger turtles lay 15 to 25 eggs. Snapping turtles sometimes deposit as many as 40 eggs. The eggs are usually elliptical in shape, although snapping turtles lay round ones shaped like ping-pong balls. They are covered with a tough, leather-like skin instead of shell.

Turtles love life lasts as long as courtship and then the former love is forgotten. The female also ignores the eggs once they are laid. Some turtles have interesting courtship activities. For instance, the male of the common painted turtle grows long fingernails in spring to thrill his love by scratching her face.

Many turtles make interesting pets, readily taking food out of man's hands. The practice of painting the young should be discontinued, however, since it seriously interferes with their growth.

FISH

Names of Fishes

When a Texan says he is going trout fishing he is actually planning to go bass fishing. When a fisherman in Wisconsin brings home a string of bullheads he certainly would not think of them as horned pout. Many fishermen in New Hampshire who go shad fishing look blank when you talk about whitefish. This confusion has been compounded by the fact that sport fishermen, commercial fishermen, fish culturists, and scientific workers may, as groups, have different names for the same fish.

In 1933 the American Fisheries Society formed a committee composed of leading fisheries men in North America to "prepare and submit for publication a list of common names of fishes corresponding to the accepted scientific names". The committee members planned to publish a list of fishes, with each fish having but one common name, that name to be accepted which received a two-thirds vote of the committee. This was easier said than done. In all, 605 fishes were considered for the list, of which 35 were eliminated as not of sufficient interest to be included. Of the remaining 570, the members came to a unanimous agreement on only 245 fish, while 291 were approved by at least a two-thirds vote. The remaining 34 fish finally received a common name on the basis of a majority vote. It took the committee almost fifteen years to complete their task.

In 1948 the American Fisheries Society published the bulletin titled: *A List of Common and Scientific Names of the Better Known Fishes of the United States and Canada*. It made immense strides toward bringing order out of confusion.

In 1960, the committee brought forth a second edition, containing many important revisions to the original edition. The new publication lists 1,892 species of fish, of which 616 are listed as occurring in fresh water at some time of their life, and the remainder as marine species inhabiting shore waters of North America on or above the continental shelf, to a depth of 100 fathoms.

This edition may be purchased for $1.00 each (paper cover) or $2.00 each (cloth cover) from the American Fisheries Society, Box 483, McLean, Virginia.

Fishes in New Hampshire

There are currently at least sixty different species of fresh-water fish in New Hampshire waters. Twenty-six of these are game and pan fish, among which are six kinds of salmonoids (trout and salmon), six kinds of sunfish, and two species of horned pout.

To the amazement of many, New Hampshire's only true fresh-water bass is the white perch, while smallmouth and largemouth bass are actually of the sunfish family. Brown trout and rainbow trout belong to the salmon family, and the so-called shad in Lake Winnipesaukee are really whitefish.

The bridled shiner is perhaps New Hampshire's smallest fish, seldom growing more than two inches in length, while the lake trout can become New Hampshire's largest fish. There have been reports of specimens caught in the United States which weighed in the vicinity of a hundred pounds.

Carp and minnows belong to the same family, of which sixteen occur in New Hampshire; also, four different suckers are found in this State.

Several species once found in New Hampshire are now no longer a part of our fauna; namely, Atlantic Sturgeon, Atlantic Salmon, American Shad. The Chinook Salmon was once introduced, flour-ished for a while, and then disappeared. The northern pike, blue-gill, black crappie, and rock bass are non-residents that crop up from time to time, particularly along the Connecticut and Merri-mack Rivers. Then there are several other invaders who seem to have acquired a permanent foothold in New Hampshire and of whom we shall probably hear more in the years to come. These are the carp, goldfish, and the walleye.

Ocean Fishes

Why do New Englanders spend hundreds of thousand dollars for fish hatcheries and rearing pools and neglect the greatest rearing pool on earth, right at their doorsteps? On our shores lies a mighty ocean with unlimited food resources, with no space problems, its salty waters counteracting many diseases common to freshwater hatcheries, and with vast hordes of fish which it once sent into streams up and down its coastline. Atlantic salmon, shad, alewives, and eel were all once a sought-after food resource of early settlers. There are rainbow, brook, and brown trout living in coastal streams that do not at all hesitate spending part of their lives in the ocean. Here their growth is so prodigious that they hardly resemble our fresh water trout when they return to spawn in the streams of their origin.

Striped bass will come into New England's estuaries, often surpassing in size and fight any of our freshwater fishes.

Any one or all of these fish species can be brought back into the streams of our land which now empty into the ocean. Modern fish and game departments have the know-how to bring this about, if but two stumbling blocks are removed. The filth and sludge now emptied into our rivers must be controlled. No self-respecting salmonoid will brave the present mess. Once pollution has come under control, attention must be given to dams blocking free passageway. Fishways will have to be built in dams now in existence. In the meantime, fish and game departments are already planning for the future. When any new dams are now built on interstate waters, the Federal Power Commission is asked to stipulate that the permittee must construct a suitable fishway or ladder, if and when dams down river get fishways.

The Atlantic Ocean is there for us to use, sans feeding bills, maintenance, and fear of water shortages.

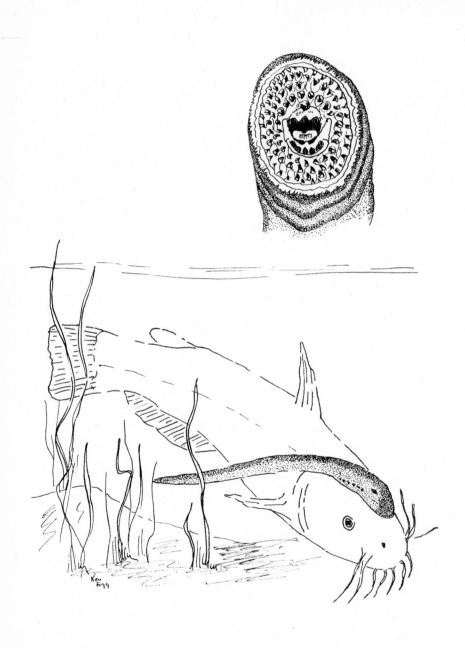

Lamprey

When the engineers finished construction of the Welland Canal in 1829 no one would have dreamed that this might some day indirectly cause the ruination of the lake trout fisheries in the Great Lakes. Not only did the canal provide passageway for ships between Lake Erie and Lake Ontario, but it also opened up these lakes to the dreaded sea lamprey which prior to that time were prevented from getting into the Lakes by Niagara Falls. It took the lamprey about a hundred years to take over. The first known spawning population was observed in a tributary to Lake Erie in 1932, and by that time it was too late. Between 1935 and 1948 the lake trout fishery dwindled, in Lake Huron alone, from 1,743,000 pounds a year to 4,000 pounds a year. Of course, many other species of fish have been affected. It represented a many million dollars a year loss to the commercial fishing industry.

In recent years an intensive research program has been in progress to develop ways and means to combat this predator. First, it was necessary to learn as much as possible about this creature's habits and its life history in order to find out where it might be most vulnerable to control measures. It is now the consensus that the sea lamprey is most vulnerable during its immature stage, before it becomes a parasitic adult. Two control measures seem to offer the greatest promise of success. One is the use of electric currents in the breeder streams. Of still greater promise is the discovery of a selective poison which seems to affect only the young lampreys, but not other species of fish. A total of 4,346 chemicals was tested in an effort to find such a poison. Not only was the search a success, but the study brought to light other poisons which may eventually revolutionize the present technique of reclaiming ponds for fish.

There are at least 13 different species of lampreys in North America, of which only 6 are parasitic. The non-parasitic type are generally small and are found in smaller streams, while the parasitic species are more apt to occur in large bodies of water. Best known of them all, and the one which has been responsible for the tremendous damage in the Great Lakes, is the Sea Lamprey. These fish have long been known in the streams entering the Atlantic Ocean, where they have been taken as far south

as northern Florida. Although they normally spend their adult life in the ocean, they have adapted themselves to living in freshwater lakes. For instance, before invading the Great Lakes they were already well known in Lake Ontario.

This lamprey has a smooth, scaleless body. While the adults are mottled in coloration, this mottling does not appear until the lamprey is about a foot long. The Sea Lamprey reaches a maximum length of about three feet and may weigh up to two pounds. Instead of a mouth with jaws, the lamprey has a round sucking disc, from the center of which rows of sharp, horny teeth radiate in all directions. One to three larger teeth are on the palate, and the tongue is file-like. Close behind each eye of the adult is a row of seven circular gill openings through which the lamprey breathes. A single nostril on top of the head is a blind sac.

Sea Lampreys attain their full growth in the Atlantic Ocean and various large lakes, where attaching themselves to fish they gorge on their blood and body fluids. Two glands in the mouth secrete a substance which keeps the blood of their victims from coagulating. When the lampreys become sexually mature, they begin a leisurely migration up streams and rivers to spawn. This occurs in spring. They travel mainly at night, from time to time attaching themselves to rock walls and other objects to rest. Sometimes they may even hitch a ride by attaching themselves to boats. They can be observed in various tributaries entering our Great Bay and the Ocean. During this time they do little if any feeding.

When their destination is reached, consisting of unpolluted streams with gravelly bottoms, they proceed with the task of building nests, generally in shallow water down to about three feet in depth. They uproot the larger stones, and with their sucking mouth they remove smaller stones to form 3 to 6 inch crescent-shaped depressions. Here the eggs are laid. A large lamprey can lay as many as 200,000 eggs. Then the adult lampreys die.

The eggs of the Sea Lamprey hatch in about ten days. The eyeless, toothless larval forms are called ammocoetes. They stay in the nest until they are about half-an-inch long, which takes about a month. Then the young begin to drift downstream, finally to burrow into mud or silt flats where they will spend about four years of their life feeding on small organisms brought to them by the current of the river. At this time they are called "mud-eels", "mud lampreys", or "sand lampreys".

When they reach a length of about 4 to 7 inches, they begin to change into the adult form, with the mouth becoming circular. The transformed lamprey now leave their burrows, generally in spring, and migrate downstream into the ocean or lake. Here they seek out a victim and attach themselves. When they first hook on to a fish, the victim will make violent efforts to rub its tormentor off, but generally to no avail. They will stay here until the fish dies or until lampreys have become glutted. When they release their hold the fish will be left with circular wounds which spoil them for commercial use. Although it is not known for certain how long this stage lasts, there is some evidence that the lamprey is ready to head for its spawning grounds about eighteen months after it has entered the ocean.

The nonparasitic lampreys found in small brooks differ mainly from their larger parasitic cousins in that as soon as they transform from the ammocoete stage to the adult form they migrate upstream to mate and die.

The Sea Lamprey was formerly used as food by many of the early settlers, and is still sought after by people in certain European countries. Its meat is not too popular in the United States.

Anyone wishing to learn more about these interesting creatures can get much information from two publications put out by the Bureau of Sport Fisheries and Wildlife. Fishery Leaflet 360 by Lola Tidwell Dees is titled *Sea Lampreys of the Atlantic Coast and Great Lakes,* and Fishery Leaflet 384 by Vernon C. Applegate is titled *The Sea Lamprey in the Great Lakes.*

Shad

If we had lived a hundred years ago, many of us in New Hampshire would probably head for Amoskeag Falls or for The Weirs around apple blossom time and when the shadfly arrived, in order to get our annual supply of shad coming from the ocean in vast hordes up the major rivers to spawn. It would be a time of merriment, many an individual bringing a gallon or two of rum to keep from catching cold. This member of the Herring Family was so common an article of diet that it was said that in the spring people could not get their shirts off without help, because of the shad bones that stuck out of their flesh, like porcupine quills. This ample supply of fish meat, along with the fun and revelry that went with gathering it, gradually disappeared when dams were built in the major rivers, blocking out the shad runs. Later efforts at restoring these runs through the construction of fishways were then further thwarted by pollution.

The American Shad ranges from the Gulf of St. Lawrence to Florida. In 1871 this fish was introduced along the Pacific Coast, where it thrived and spread, so that it is now found from southern California to southeastern Alaska. This fish lives in salt water and spawns in fresh water. The spawning run starts in southern rivers first, about mid-November. As the season progresses shad gradually appear northward, entering northern rivers about May or June. The favorite spawning grounds are on sandy flats, particularly where brooks enter the rivers. The shad move up to the flats in pairs, generally between sundown and midnight. The spawning act is accompanied by considerable splashing which can be plainly heard from the shore. No nest is built, the eggs simply being extruded hit or miss. One female, depending on her size, may lay over 100,000 eggs. It takes the eggs between 3 and 10 days to hatch, depending on the water temperature. The old shad return to sea about August, while the young go to sea in autumn.

After they return to the ocean, there seems to be a northward movement, the shad spending the summer off the New England coast, migrating south along the Continental shelf during winter to Georgia, moving shoreward and once again migrating northward. They mature the third or fourth year, and it is believed they return to spawn in the same stream in which they originated.

201

Whitefish

As a whole, fish take a back seat to furbearers and game animals in New Hampshire during the winter months. Not so the white-fish, or "shad" as this fish is called in our state. Unlike most other game fishes, the whitefish is fished mainly in winter when ice is thick enough to hold bob houses. To the novice who for the first time tries his luck at this type of fishing, it is a constant source of amazement to see how delicately the whitefish tugs at the baited hook. As he watches the "corset stave" to which the line is often attached, he finds it hard to differentiate between the gentle undulations of the stave caused by wave action and the slightly more irregular movements caused by the fish on the hook. If he then heeds the warning of the old-timer who tells him to "pull her up", and after hauling in about seventy feet of line finds a foot long fish on the end of it, he is apt to be flabber-gasted. He will hardly ever disagree with other fishermen who emphatically state that "shad" are delicious.

There are two kinds in New Hampshire, the Inland Lakes Whitefish and the rarer Round Whitefish. They closely resemble each other. Both are found only in some of our larger and deeper lakes, although the latter is occasionally taken from the upper Connecticut River where it is known as Billfish, and from the Cockermouth River flowing into Newfound Lake.

Since we know very little about our whitefish in New Hamp-shire, we must rely on information concerning it from studies made elsewhere. It has been of great importance commercially in the Great Lakes. One was taken from Lake Superior having attained the record weight of twenty-six pounds. The smallness of their mouths and weakness of their teeth indicate that white-fish feed mainly on plankton, small crustaceans, and insects. They spawn sometime between October and December, when they move to shallow water. The females rise to the surface a number of times and liberate their eggs. These float near the surface.

In the course of his studies, Biologist Ronald Towne had an opportunity to gather information relative to this fish in Squam Lakes, some of which seems to throw some new light on the habits of our "shad". He found, for instance, that the immature whitefish travel around in schools, that they generally seem to

mature in their third year when they are about one foot long, and average ten ounces in weight. In Squam Lakes they reach peak spawning activities in December and this activity takes place at night. Particularly interesting was the fact that Towne found smelt and remains of other fish in many shad he examined during the winter months.

In a paper titled, *The Relative Strengths of Whitefish Year Classes as Affected by Egg Plantings and Weather*, Richard B. Miller made some important contributions to our knowledge of this fish. He did his work in six different Alberta Lakes in Canada. He found, for example, that the planting of whitefish eggs in a lake which already has this fish has little if any effect on the total population present.

Miller found that in certain years there was a scarcity of young whitefish (or "tinkers"), and this scarcity was common to all six lakes he studied. In years in which these "tinkers" were numerous, they were so in all six lakes. Fishermen in New Hampshire have observed this same phenomenon and, like Miller, have asked themselves "why"? Since he observed this low or high population to occur simultaneously in all six study lakes, Miller reasoned that there had to be some factor which affected all lakes at the same time, and one such factor was wind. It must be kept in mind that whitefish come to shallow areas and lay their eggs near the surface of the water where they are free floating. Miller noticed that in years when there were many strong winds in late autumn, wind rows of whitefish eggs could be found along the lake shores and the following year there would be a decided drop in numbers of young whitefish. He stated, however, that more studies were needed to establish this fact for a surety.

It might pay New Hampshire "shad" fishermen to keep a record of wind velocities in late November and December to see how these affect future whitefish populations.

Atlantic Salmon

Most every schoolboy has heard of the great salmon runs that occurred in New England's rivers during the last century, until dams and pollution stopped them. Today but a few rivers, such as the Miramichi in New Brunswick and the Penobscot in Maine, still harbor this beautiful game fish.

The Atlantic Salmon is also a native of northern Europe. In the western Atlantic Ocean they range from the Polar regions south to Cape Cod. Where these fish go during their sojourn in the ocean is not too well known.

After spending several years in the ocean, salmon return to fresh-water rivers to spawn. Some return after only one winter at sea. These adolescent fish are then known as "grilse", and at this age are very vigorous and active, almost coltish, in their actions. Most salmon, however, return after three or more years at sea and are then mature fish. While they are in the estuaries and mouths of rivers they will rise to artificial flies. When they ascend the fresh-water rivers to spawn, they seldom take food.

They ascend fresh-water rivers at all times of the year, although these runs reach a peak in June in northern New England. Spawning time takes place in late autumn, sometime between late October and December. At this time the urge to reach the headwaters is so strong that salmon have been known to leap over perpendicular obstacles 18 feet high. They select gravel bottom areas with fast currents. Here the females scoop out troughs with their tails while the males fight each other. The female then lays eggs into these troughs while a male a short distance behind her fertilizes the eggs. These are then covered with gravel. This process continues mostly at night for several days, since all the eggs are not extruded at once. After spawning is completed the spent adult fish are called "kelt". Many stay until spring before going back to sea. A few may return to spawn twice or even three times during a lifetime. About 900 eggs are laid per each pound of body weight. The eggs hatch in late winter or early spring. The fry remain hidden in crevices and beneath stones. Within a few months the fry reach the "parr" stage, during which time they swim about freely. At the end of the second winter they go down to sea, at which time they are known as "smolts". Then for several years they eat and grow.

Rainbow Trout

It is much easier to catch a rainbow trout than it is to write about it. So mixed up is this fish's background that fisheries specialists are still arguing about it. For the most they agree, however, that the distribution of rainbows was formerly restricted to that part of North America west of the Rocky Mountains, that they spent part of their life in the Pacific Ocean, and like salmon ascended the freshwater streams to spawn. Unlike Pacific Salmon, which spawned once and then died, rainbow trout (or steelheads) could return to the ocean to spawn again another day. In fact, some did not return to the ocean but developed the ability to live their entire life in fresh water. Today we differentiate between those that annually return to the ocean, where they grow more rapidly than in fresh water, by calling them Steelhead Trout, which their slower-growing fresh-water cousins are called Rainbow Trout.

Since these trout were easily propagated in hatcheries, and because of their superb sporting qualities, it was only natural that attempts would have been made to introduce them into new areas. So successful were these efforts that today the rainbow trout is found in all parts of this continent, where water temperatures of streams or lakes do not exceed 80° F. and preferably stay below 70° F.

Rainbow spawning normally begins in early winter and reaches a peak in spring. Today, however, with hatchery manipulation of spawning activities, one may even find fall spawning rainbows. They show a tendency to migrate upstream at such times, seeking swift waters and clean gravel, preferably at the lower end of pools. The female digs pits (redds) in the gravel while the male stays nearby. When the eggs are laid the male immediately fertilizes them and the female covers them with gravel, often up to eight inches in depth. Other pits may then be dug until the female has finished laying. The whole process may take several days. The length of time it takes the eggs to hatch depends on the water temperature — fifty to sixty days being not unusual. Males may reach maturity their second year, while females generally wait until their third year.

A 37 pound rainbow trout in the western states would approach the world record, while you need catch only a 15-pounder in New Hampshire to do the same.

Brown Trout

The first shipment of brown trout to New Hampshire was probably imported from Germany in 1887. It is still a moot question whether our state would be better off if brown trout had never been planted in our streams. Calvin Hall, who caught a 15 pound, 6 ounce brown below the Murphy Dam in Pittsburg in 1953, will probably be emphatic in saying that no mistake was made, but the many less fortunate fishermen who have seen the brown crowd out brook trout or salmon are apt to be more dubious about the matter.

Maine's Department of Inland Fisheries and Game recently published a bulletin *The Brown Trout in Maine* which aptly discusses some of the problems involved when brown trout are introduced. It should first of all be recognized that the requirements of this fish are very similar to those of the landlocked salmon, except that the brown can tolerate somewhat warmer waters. They spawn from the latter part of October to February. Prior to spawning, males will start to defend their chosen territories against rivals. In the meanwhile the female digs egg pits in the loose rubble, using her tail and body as an excavator. Large females often dig three or four such pits which are up to twelve inches deep. These nesting areas are called redds. Each egg pit is constructed so that an eddy current is set up inside, holding the eggs and milt firmly in the bottom despite swift currents. A large female may lay over 3,000 eggs. These she covers with gravel.

The young hatch out the following spring and spend their first two or three years of life in the stream feeding on small insects and animal life. Later, moving into lakes, they gradually feed more on fish life. Once established in lakes they tend to grow faster than salmon and become increasingly difficult to catch. Only highly skilled fishermen are able to take the large brown trout. These consume tremendous amounts of food.

The brown trout is a poor investment in terms of returns to fishermen. Maine stocked a series of reclaimed ponds with brook trout and other ponds with brown trout. Approximately five brook trout were caught to every one brown trout. Our major concern should be to keep this fish out of our established landlocked salmon lakes. Brown trout are apt to crowd out salmon.

Sunapee Trout

The Sunapee, or Golden Trout has been truly a fish of mystery. Originally described from Sunapee Lake in New Hampshire, it is also known to have occurred in Big Dan Hole Pond, N. H., Averill Lake in Vermont, and Floods Pond in Maine. And that is all! Where did it come from? Was Sunapee Lake its birthplace? How closely is this trout related to the common Brook Trout or the Lake Trout? It is known that the three can hybridize under artificial conditions. Or is it more closely related to the Blueback or the Red Quebec Trout with which it has many characteristics in common. Why have the Sunapee Trout's spawning requirements been so exacting? The Fish and Game Department has never found it to spawn in numbers except on one reef, composed of rubble, boulders, and gravel approaching to within several inches of the lake's surface.

Spawning has generally occurred between October 20 and November 20, and most often reaching a peak about October 27, when water temperatures hovered around 48°F. A female averages about 1,200 eggs per pound of fish. The spawning habits of the Sunapee Trout are very much like those of the Lake Trout. Both use the same reef in Sunapee Lake. After the eggs have been deposited among the rocks, the adult trout leave the reef, and the emerging fry must fend for themselves. The approximate period of incubation in hatcheries in water temperatures of 44°F. has been 80 days.

Although the Sunapee Trout live most of their lives in the deepest parts of the lake, around 90 to 100 feet, they are found near the surface in spring. This occurs when their main source of food, the American smelt, is there too, to spawn.

The two main methods of angling for this fish have been through trolling, and by bobbing cut and live bait in deep water.

Wherever Lake Trout have become numerous, Golden Trout have declined in numbers. This seems to be happening in Lake Sunapee. The New Hampshire Fish and Game Department is making every effort to keep this fish from joining the extinct Agassiz Trout. At present an attempt to foster the growth of the Sunapee Trout in Tewksbury Pond in Grafton appears to be meeting with considerable success.

Brook Trout

Furbearers, game birds, in fact most animal species seem to fade into the background in the spring while an old native of New Hampshire rockets into the limelight. On opening day of the season, brook trout is king supreme and we his subjects.

The reason for this should make an interesting subject for research into the behavior patterns of the human animal. There are a large number of good, sound, perfectly sensible reasons — each as illogical as the other, so there is no need to go into the subject too deeply. Instead, let's examine the source of all this excitement.

The brook trout is found in our most picturesque waters. Cold ponds and streams are the natural home of this fish. Climb the Presidential Range and leave horned pout, bass, and even rainbow trout far below you, the scrappy little "brookie" will be up there where scenery is grandest. It prefers to live in waters with a mean temperature of around 58°F. and where maximum temperatures seldom go over 66°F. In fact, the waters over 70°F. soon become fatal to this fish.

The trout breeds in fall. In late August and September it begins to migrate upstream to seek gravel-bottomed areas in spring-fed branches. Those living in ponds and lakes move into tributaries, or will even spawn along gravelly shores, especially where spring water seeps up. Trout do not naturally migrate upstream but do so because suitable spawning areas are usually found there. If good areas occur downstream, trout are just as apt to move in that direction, as has been indicated in our own studies in the Swift River by biologist Arthur Newell.

When the fish are ready to spawn the female prepares a nest by turning on her side and rapidly moving her head and tail up and down. In this manner she dislodges the gravel. The completed nest will be a foot or two in diameter and several inches deep. When the eggs are first extruded they are sticky, which attaches them to the gravel in the nest. After they become water hardened they lose their adhesive quality. About fifty days later, more or less, depending on the temperature of the water, the fry hatch and work up through the gravel.

If anyone catches a brook trout weighing more than 14 pounds he might have a world's record.

Lake Trout

In New Hampshire when fishermen really let their imaginations run wild and talk about "monsters" in our larger lakes, they generally have lake trout in mind. Many an old timer has his pet tale about the time he was trolling deep with copper wire, when suddenly there was a terrific yank and the wire snapped in two. Each spring, hardly an issue of our larger newspapers passes by without pictures of some big ones. Fisheries biologist, Ronald Towne, who devoted several years of study to fish in Squam Lake, states that he had records of several 14-pounders out of Squam, and one which tipped the scales at 19. The largest one recorded for New Hampshire in the Fish and Game Office weighed 28½ lbs., caught out of Newfound Lake in 1958.

It is difficult to generalize about this fish since its habits, its growth and even its color vary so from one lake to another. In Lake Opengo in Ontario, lake trout reach maturity sometime between their sixth and eighth year, while in Great Bear Lake in Canada they do not mature until they are somewhere between 13 and 17 years old, at which time they weigh about two pounds. Towne found, on the other hand, that in Squam Lake this trout spawns for the first time in its sixth year, when it is about two feet long and weighs about four pounds.

Spawning generally occurs on reefs or along rubble-strewn shores. In Squam Lake males begin to come to the reefs in late October, the females come somewhat later. Towne states that peak spawning occurred on the nights of November 4 and 5 several years in a row, when water temperature was 47°F. Lake trout are not highly prolific, when compared to other species of fish. The first spawning will produce only about 1000 eggs. These settle down between rocks and rubble. The incubation period will depend much on the water temperature, ranging from fifty days in 50°F. water to about 160 in 35°F. water. The young grow slowly, spending their first four summers in shallow water near shore. At first, plankton is their main food. As they grow larger they devour practically anything that moves, before they are finally eaten by us.

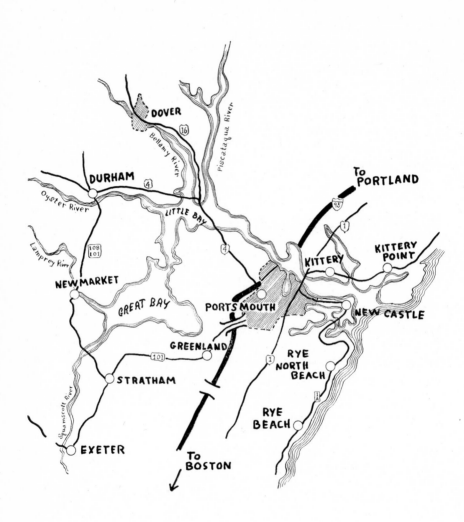

DOVER

Piscataqua River

Bellamy River

16

DURHAM

4

Oyster River

LITTLE BAY

To PORTLAND

95

1

4

KITTERY

KITTERY POINT

108
101

Lamprey River

NEWMARKET

GREAT BAY

PORTSMOUTH

NEW CASTLE

GREENLAND

101

RYE NORTH BEACH

1

STRATHAM

Squamscott River

1A

RYE BEACH

1A

EXETER

To BOSTON

Sea-Run Trout

Some day pollution in the Great Bay and its tributary streams may be cleaned up. When that time comes, New Hampshire will want to give a great deal of attention to the possibility of establishing "sea-run" trout in these streams. In the meantime, there are persistent rumors to the effect that an occasional "salter" is caught out of our coastal streams. Although fishermen from whom these rumors originate are understandably reticent about giving out concrete information, we go on the assumption that where there is smoke there might be a fire. With this in mind, it might be well to review an article recently appearing in *New Jersey Outdoors*, written by fisheries biologist Bruce Pyle.

He states the sea-run trout are not uncommon in streams along northern New England and southeastern Canada as far north as the Nelson River. New Jersey seems to be the most southern limit from which these trout have been reported. All of us have, of course, heard about the steelhead rainbow trout on the Pacific Coast, found from the Mexico-California border to northern Alaska. Here in New England, "salters" may be either brook (also called speckled trout), rainbow or brown trout. There is no taxonomic difference between these and their cousins which live entirely in fresh water. The only difference is that one moves down into salt, or brackish water, and the other does not. "Fresh-run" trout (those having just returned from salt water) have a distinct silvery appearance caused by a coating of guanin accumulated while in the salt water. Usually they are also more heavily bodied.

All sea-run trout do not descend to or ascend from the sea at exactly the same time each year. The migration depends upon the species, the age of the fish, and various environmental conditions. All three species usually descend to the sea after having spent two years in fresh water. The brook and brown trout descend from early April to June and return from late July through the fall months. After the trout leave the river very little is known about their activities.

What makes one trout migrate and another of the same species remain in the stream is still a mystery. One thing is sure, however, New Hampshire should not overlook the fact that the Atlantic Ocean might serve us as a great fish rearing pool.

Smelt

There are various kinds of smelts. They are found on both sides of the Atlantic Ocean in the northern hemisphere, and also in the Pacific Ocean. How many kinds there actually are is one of those mysteries. For one thing, it is uncertain whether the salt-water variety found along the Atlantic Coast from Virginia north to the Gulf of St. Lawrence should be considered different from the landlocked fresh-water smelt found in New England lakes and in the Great Lakes. Furthermore, anyone who has fished for fresh-water smelt will tell you that there are two kinds: "regular smelt" — which average around 3 inches, and "big smelt" that may reach a length of 14 or more inches. Outside of size, however, there is no other difference. Are all three of these varieties one and the same species?

All have essentially the same habits. Whether in the Ocean or in freshwater lakes, soon after ice-out, smelt come into the tributaries after sunset in vast numbers to spawn. Many also spawn in suitable areas along the shoreline — particularly in the Great Lakes. As a rule, first to come are the males. These can be distinguished from the females by the fact that they feel rough and prickly while the females feel smooth. In fresh water the spawning runs occur while the water temperature ranges between 35 degrees and 59 degrees Fahrenheit. Usually seeking a gravelly bottom, the males take their places over the spawning beds, moving and milling about until females appear. Their appearance generally reaches several peaks which become progressively later at night as the season wanes. Each female will deposit somewhere between 1,700 and 7,000 eggs, but no more than 50 at any one time. By morning the females will have returned to the lake; many males, however, remain in the brooks during the day. Most smelt in the spawning run are two-years old. Some oldtimers may be as old as six years. The eggs may hatch anywhere from one to six weeks, depending on the temperature. Soon after they hatch, the fry are carried downstream by the current.

Although most smelt are taken by dip nets and other devices during their spawning runs, many are caught by hook and line through the ice in winter. Smelt feed on small crustaceans, small fish, fish eggs, and plankton. A characteristic of smelts is their cucumber or violet-like smell.

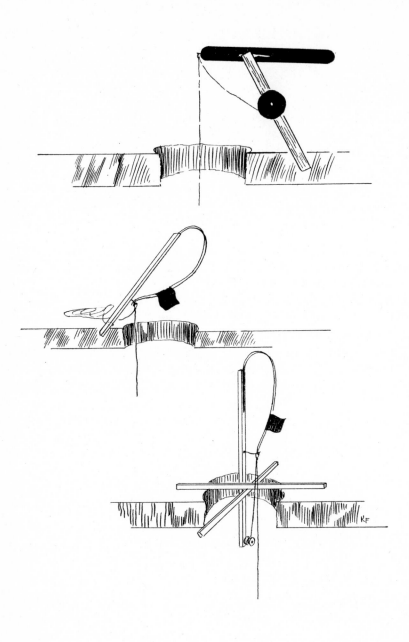

Pickerel

On the basis of a recent survey conducted (1955) by the New Hampshire Fish and Game Department, it was determined that the pickerel ranks third in popularity as a game fish in New Hampshire with residents and nonresidents alike.

There are two species of pickerel in New Hampshire: the common chain pickerel found throughout the state, and the small bulldog pickerel found in the southeastern section. Another member of the family, the northern pike, is occasionally caught in the Connecticut River. Main interest is expressed in the chain pickerel, which spawns early in the spring when water temperatures are about 47° F. The eggs are scattered among vegetation or submerged branches. A two-pound female will lay about 30,000 eggs. These hatch in six to twelve days, depending on water temperatures. Although the newly hatched fry are able to swim almost immediately, they generally lie on their sides on the bottom of the lake or pond during the day and rise toward the surface at night and attach themselves to debris, probably with a gummy secretion. The yolk sac is absorbed in about six to eight days, when feeding commences. From that time on the pickerel will grow rapidly.

By the end of June the young pickerel will average about 1½ inches in size and about 4 inches by the end of September. Some mature when they are one year old while others are still immature in their third year. By the fourth year all have probably reached spawning age. In some lakes the pickerel spawn before they are 12 inches long, but in areas where growing conditions are good they may not spawn until they are about 14 inches in length. Anyone catching a pickerel in this state weighing more than 7 pounds will have a New Hampshire record. The present world's record for this species is 9 lbs. 5 oz., taken in Massachusetts through the ice.

Young pickerel eat many insects, but adults feed mainly on fish, crayfish, and frogs. Anglers who fail to catch pickerel in midsummer often claim that these fish are growing new teeth and have sore gums. Since pickerel have about the same number of teeth throughout the year, their canine teeth constantly in the process of being replaced by newly developing teeth, the fisherman had better change his excuse to the fact there is so much other food available at that time of year.

Fallfish

Have you ever come across piles of stones in a river and wondered what made them? Wade down the Blackwater or the Suncook River, for instance, and you will see a number of these stone piles, looking as if they had been dumped there with a wheelbarrow. The stones vary in size from small pebbles to several inches in diameter and some piles are three to four feet in diameter and more than a foot high.

It is difficult to imagine that these are nests made by our common chub or fallfish. In May the males pick up, with their mouths, stones weighing anywhere from an ounce to a pound and deposit them in these piles to be used as communal nests. During spawning the fish gather in crowds, many fish using one nest. During the breeding season the males can be distinguished from the females by small growths or tubercles on their snouts.

The fallfish is one of the most common fishes in New Hampshire, found in both streams and lakes. This fish is often found near rapids and falls — from whence the name "fallfish". It varies considerably in size. In small brooks, mature fallfish may be only a few inches in length, while in larger rivers they may reach a length of two feet.

They will strike at the same lure as trout — from live bait to artificial flies. Many a trout fisherman has got "a beautiful strike", played the fish carefully, and finally netted it to find he had a "lousy, blankety-blank fallfish". We have even found one happy out-of-state fisherman with his limit of "trout", and did not have the heart to tell him what his "trout" actually were. They probably tasted good, too, although quite some bonier than trout.

This fish is utilized as food by many game fish, loons, mergansers and herons. It is valuable, in its place; but a pest when it gets into a reclaimed trout pond.

Suckers

My fondest boyhood memories of early spring are of Saturdays spent along the LaCrosse River in Wisconsin, fishing for suckers. Shortly after ice-out, and as soon as angleworms could be found, river banks would suddenly become alive with small boys, town characters, grandfathers, and cane poles. While we waited for suckers to bite we would sit against the sunny side of trees watching willow and poplar catkins unfold, redwing blackbirds stake out their claims in adjacent cattail marshes, and the gentle undulation of our line in the muddy water, always hoping for that telltale jerk. Suckers have a sweet and delicately flavored meat, although it is somewhat boney. It is a pity that so few boys in New Hampshire experience the lazy delight of cane pole fishing for suckers. By going after these fish, boys could be doing double duty; namely, thinning down an overabundance of these fish in our waters and providing their family with a high protein food. Even the roe of suckers, fried in butter, is a delicacy.

There are four kinds of suckers in New Hampshire: the northern sturgeon sucker, its very close relative the dwarf sturgeon sucker, the creek chubsucker, and most common of them all, the white sucker. They are found both in streams and lakes, where they feed on bottom organisms, such as insects, clams and worms.

Suckers spawn in spring from April to June, about the time the water temperature gets around 45° F. Although they will spawn in lakes in the absence of inlets, they prefer to migrate up streams if these are present. They generally reach maturity sometime after their third year, the males usually maturing one year earlier. As a rule the males are smaller than the females. Their greatest spawning activity is between dusk and 11:00 P.M. A sixteen to twenty-one inch sucker will lay from 20,000 to 50,000 eggs. They are deposited promiscuously in sand and gravel and are left unattended. These will hatch in six to seven days if the water is from 57° to 68° F.

This is to suggest that New Hampshire boys try sucker fishing in April.

Horned Pout

Outside of New England they are called bullheads, but here they are known as horned pout. Some fishermen act as if horned pout come from the wrong side of the railroad track; nevertheless, it is the second most sought after fish in the state by resident fishermen. In New Hampshire there are two kinds — the common brown horned pout, found all over the state, and the less common yellow horned pout found in certain areas of southern New Hampshire. They are most easily found at night.

The breeding habits of this fish are interesting. Sometime in May or June the males become pugnacious. Many come out of battles with scarred heads where other males clamped down on them. The paired fish then begin to construct nests, generally along the shore in water several inches to several feet in depth, or under stumps or logs. Sometimes a cove may contain a number of nests close to one another. If the nest site contains gravel this is carried away by mouth until the bottom is smooth. The female then lays her several clusters of frog-like eggs in the depression, numbering anywhere from about 50 to more than a thousand eggs. In 77° F. or warmer water these hatch in from twenty-four hours to five or more days. There are good parents and poor parents, just like humans. In some cases the female will guard the eggs and desert the nest when these hatch, while the male takes over. In other cases both guard the eggs and the hatched young. The newly hatched young remain on the bottom in dense masses until they are about six days old, when they begin to swim vertically several inches and then fall back. Soon they are swimming actively in dense schools. From the time of hatching the parents keep the fry agitated constantly by a gentle fanning motion of lower fins and at intervals stir them with their barbels. The parents will also suck the eggs and the newly hatched fry into their mouth and blow them out again. As time goes on the adults' parental instincts begin to vanish when the tendency to suck the fry into their mouths continues, but the inclination to spit them out diminishes. As the fry increase in size they have a tendency to congregate.

Horned pout are very tenacious of life. They can live in ponds that dry up by lying dormant in a clod of mud until softened by the return of water. They seem to hibernate in winter, burying themselves in the deepest ooze of the pond.

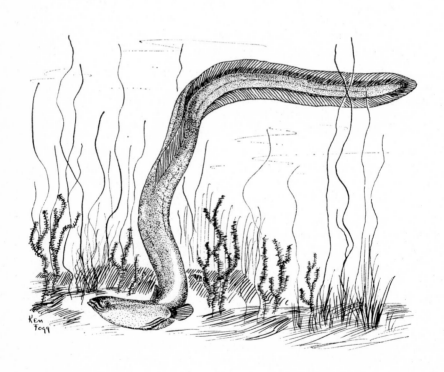

Eel

The fisherman who has accidentally hooked on to a large eel, pulled it into his boat, and then felt like jumping out leaving the long, slithering, and winding fish in complete charge of the situation may not consider this fish particularly interesting. Actually, the American eel is one of New Hampshire's most amazing fishes.

The flesh of eels is considered a delicacy by many. Eels are found in the Mississippi Valley and to the Atlantic Coast, but not along the Pacific Coast. They are also found along the West Coast of Europe. Not only are they powerful swimmers, but are also able to wriggle short distances across land, sometimes being found in damp lowlands in search of frogs, crayfish, and other foods.

In the past the eel was truly a fish of mystery, since no one knew what its young looked like, or at least thought he didn't. However, in the middle of the Atlantic Ocean biologists had from time to time caught a strange little ribbon or leaf like organism, perfectly transparent and having colorless blood. Some called it a "glassfish". Finally a Danish oceanographer discovered that eels migrated to the Sargasso Sea and it was then learned for the first time that these "glassfish" were young eels.

These fish spend from 5 to 25 years in fresh water. Finally there comes a day when something causes the eel to give up its normal life, take to the rivers, and follow them down to the ocean. Near the mouth of the river these eels change from their yellowish color to a silvery color and are hence known as "silver eels". They then start on their last long journey, one that ends up in the abyss under the Sargasso Sea in the middle of the Atlantic Ocean. Here the females lay up to 10,000,000 eggs, each, about the size of a small pea. The spawning grounds of the European and American eel are separate but adjacent. When the little eels hatch they are carried southward and eventually find themselves in the Gulf Stream. This current then carries them on their journey to the north, so that by the time the elvers start up the rivers of the North American side of the ocean they are just about one year old. However, the larvae of the European eel continue with the Gulf Stream, and not until two years later, when they near the rivers of Western Europe and are three years old, do they transform and migrate into fresh water.

229

Cusk

Ling, burbot, lawyer, mud blower, fresh-water cod, are just some of the names given this species of fish. In New Hampshire this cousin to the cod is called "cusk". It inhabits cold lakes and streams in northern Canada from the eastern portion of Hudson Bay east to Labrador, southward to the Connecticut, Delaware, and Susquehanna system, westward to the Missouri River system, south to Missouri, Kansas and Wyoming.

Many people avoid the cusk because it is an unusual looking fish. Actually, this fish has a clean, firm flesh. Cusk livers are a rich source of vitamins. In some sections of the country cusk are netted, filleted and sold commercially. There are a number of New Hampshire fishermen who thoroughly enjoy fishing for cusk in winter through the ice. The best method of fishing seems to be with live bait near the bottom. Some fishermen claim there is nothing that will beat this fish in a chowder.

Cusk are very predaceous in habit, often devouring fish almost their own size. They do much to help control rough fish. They also eat crustaceans and eggs of other fish.

The cusk spawns sometime between November and April. A study made of these fish in a lake in Ontario, Canada, indicated that they generally spawned the last two weeks in January. During the spawning season the female, which is larger than the male, moves into sandy shallows and up streams at night, followed by various males. She is very prolific, passing off anywhere from 50,000 to 1,000,000 eggs. Incubation lasts from three to four weeks. The fry hatch and grow in the shallows without parental protection, but the young soon migrate out to deeper water.

Cusk can grow up to forty inches in length and have been caught weighing as much as twenty pounds. The one barbel on the chin serves as a feeler.

Striped Bass

New Hampshire has a small but ardent group of striped bass fishermen, as those who have watched fishermen on the Great Bay Bridges with their salt-water gear can attest to. This fish has great appeal not only because of its delicate, sweet flavor, but because one never knows when he may snag on to a real tackle-buster. Some have been known to reach a weight of 125 pounds.

Although this fish is distributed from Canada to Florida, into the Gulf of Mexico, and even on the Pacific Coast, it is most abundant in Chesapeake Bay. For this reason it is of prime importance to the State of Maryland which devotes considerable study to it, and recently published a brief informative page titled "Life History of the Striped Bass in Maryland Waters", from which most of the following information was derived.

Striped bass spawn at the head of tidewater streams from April through June, depending on water temperatures. Females usually spawn for the first time when four years old (about 17 inches long). During the spawning act a single large female, called "cow rock", is surrounded by a few to several dozen small males or "bucks". The "rock fights" which ensue are courtship antics and are accompanied by the depositing of greenish colored eggs that are heavier than water. The eggs hatch in about two days at a water temperature of about 65° F. The number produced by each female varies with size — a three-pounder deposits about 15,000 eggs while a fifty-pounder will deposit about 5,000,000 eggs.

The bass travel in large schools, especially after two years of age. In early spring they move out of their wintering areas, such as Chesapeake Bay and off New Jersey and New York, and travel northeastward to New England and southern Canada where they mingle with stocks of fish from the northern range. In autumn they move back to the Middle Atlantic States and south. Forage fish partly control their movements. They feed largely upon anchovies, menhaden, and to a lesser extent on spot, croakers, white perch, crabs and other invertebrates. During spawning season they do less feeding. Their numbers appear to increase and decrease in successive waves, depending on the success of certain hatches.

White Perch

The White Perch, *Morone americana,* is common on the Atlantic coast of North America from the Carolinas to the Gulf of St. Lawrence. It is at home in fresh, brackish, and salt water, and can be found in the lower portions of nearly all tidal streams in its range. Frequently it is landlocked in coastal ponds where it becomes purely a fresh-water fish.

A popular game fish, it takes a sunken fly readily and angle-worms, grasshoppers and small bait-fish are irresistible. When hooked it makes several fast runs and thrashes about the surface of the water vigorously, but never jumps. The White Perch is by nature a schooling fish. During the hours of daylight it seldom forsakes the deeper portions of the lake. With the coming of evening, these fish move into the shallows where they raise havoc with the small fishes in the lake. This is when the experienced angler can fill his creel. The schools move rapidly, however, and unless he can follow them or keep them there by "chumming" the fishing is over in a few minutes and the angler must wait for another school to show up. Intensive fishing for White Perch, as well as for most other warm water fish tends to improve the fishing.

The White Perch has been introduced in many of the lakes in the southern part of New Hampshire and has very often become an important fish-management problem. It has a decided tendency to overpopulate in many lakes and becomes dwarfed. In its feeding habits it is more or less competitive with most of the other game fishes in the state, and there is considerable evidence that its abundance in certain lakes is detrimental to trout and salmon populations.

When White Perch are first introduced into a body of water they usually do not show up in the sports fishery for about five years. For the next two to five years fishing for them is generally good, after which time it usually tapers off due to overpopulating and stunting.

Spawning requirements for this fish are quite simple, neither a nest nor parental care being required for the successful hatching of the eggs. All that is needed is a hard bottom to support the relatively heavy eggs and a temperature of about 53°–55° F. The incubation period, depending on the water temperature, is from two to six days.

Sunfish

No fish is more deserving of an apology from New Englanders than the sunfish. To hear the average fisherman in New Hampshire talk about this fish, one is apt to gain the impression that the sunfish is nothing but a nuisance. If the truth were known, however, nine out of ten fishermen would probably have to admit that the first fish they ever caught was a sunfish. And, perhaps, never again will fish furnish them the thrill that first one did. Sunfish are among our most colorful fresh-water fishes. They act as food to many larger game fishes. They are scrappy; willing to strike at a tremendous assortment of natural baits as well as artificial lures. On reasonably light tackle they will give an excellent account of themselves. They feed to some extent at all seasons of the year. Finally, sunfish taste good.

There is only one thing wrong with this group of fishes. They are too prolific, often crowding out more sought after game fishes. This is man's fault for not utilizing this fish to its fullest extent.

There are 19 different kinds of sunfishes in the United States and Canada, including the black basses, crappies, and at least nine different species of so-called sunfish. In New Hampshire there are, besides two species of black bass, the black crappie, rockbass, blackbanded sunfish, yellowbelly (redbreast) sunfish, pumpkinseed, and bluegill. One of the common species is the yellowbelly, known also as the redbreasted sunfish or the robin.

The spawning of this species usually takes place when the water temperature is about 72° F. The nests are located on coarse sand or gravel, generally close to the shore and in shallow water. These are often in colonies. The male fish builds the nest and then coaxes a ripe female to come to use it. As soon as the eggs are laid and fertilized, the female leaves the nest and the eggs are cared for by the male. Two or more females may spawn in the same nest.

The eggs, which are heavy and adhesive, sink to the bottom of the nest. The male fish guards the nest and fans it to keep silt from settling on them. At a water temperature of 72° F. the eggs will hatch out in four days. After about three days the fry will have absorbed the sac, and they will then swim off under the guardianship of the male parent. The fry tend to remain together in a school for the remainder of the summer. The second or third year, when they are about five inches long, they are ready to spawn.

Bluegill

Most of us are aware how great a part publicity and advertising play in the popularity of individuals in the field of entertainment. So it is also with certain fish and game species.

About twenty years ago the bluegill was just another bream or sunfish found in an area bounded roughly by Minnesota, east to Lake Champlain, south to Georgia, and west to Arkansas. In the meantime the construction of farm ponds was catching the public's fancy. The new pond owners wanted fish; somebody discovered that a combination of bass and bluegills would furnish a good self-perpetuating population of game, pan and forage fish. The Soil Conservation Service and other governmental and state agencies became the bluegill's publicity agents. Today, this sunfish is one of the nation's best known and most popular panfishes. As a result it has been stocked in ponds throughout the United States including many ponds in New Hampshire. While we must grant that its meat is very tasty, other sunfishes and, for that matter, many other panfishes are just as tasty. And while it furnishes considerable sport to many since it will take a variety of lures, its manner of biting by edging up to the bait and sucking it in leaves it much to be desired as a sport fish.

While the largest bluegill on record, caught in Alabama, was a 15-inch-long fish weighing 4 pounds and 12 ounces, the average adult is from 5 to 9 inches long. In fertile waters they attain a length of 6 inches in about three to four years. They rarely live over ten years. They thrive in shallow, weedy and warm water feeding on insects and some vegetation. They can often be heard sucking in insects with a smack of their small mouth.

Bluegills spawn in late May to early August, beginning when water temperature is about 67° F. The male generally selects a sand or gravel bar in shallow water to hollow out a nest two to six inches deep and about one foot in diameter. The female is then attracted to the nest and after a brief courtship lays her eggs. The male then maintains a constant vigil and keeps the eggs aerated and clean by fanning with the fins. The average number of eggs is about 18,000 per nest. Hatching takes about two to five days under normal weather conditions. Once hatched, the fry are protected by the male for a few additional days.

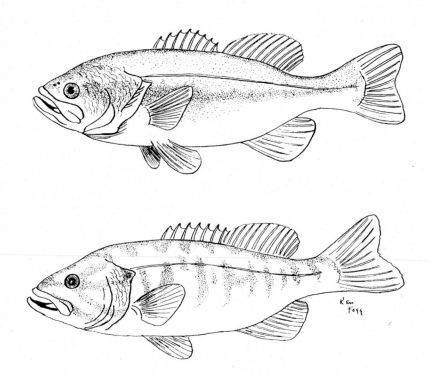

Smallmouth and Largemouth Bass

The smallmouth bass and its very close cousin, the largemouth bass, are among the prized fresh-water game fishes of North America. They are known by many different names; in fact, the smallmouth alone has 36 different names in this country. Once not so widespread, today through numerous introductions, both are found in practically every state of the Union and also in southern Canada. However, the smallmouth is missing from the Gulf States and is found somewhat farther north than the largemouth. This may be due to the fact that the former prefers larger clear water lakes or streams, while the latter can thrive in weedy ponds and sluggish streams and also in warmer water.

While both are game fighters on the end of a line, the smallmouth is more spectacular in its efforts to free itself of a fisherman's hook by leaping out of water. On the other hand, in favor of the largemouth is the fact that it can become a larger fish — one of the largest on record having weighed more than 22 pounds — while rarely does a smallmouth exceed 10 pounds in weight.

Although both look alike to the casual observer, there are some distinguishing characteristics. The joint of the jaw bone ends directly beneath the eye of the smallmouth, while it goes back beyond the eye of the largemouth. While the former has small scales on the base of the dorsal and anal fins, these scales are absent on the latter.

In New Hampshire both species spawn during May and June, for the most part when the water temperature is between 60 and 70 degrees Fahrenheit. While smallmouth bass seek gravel and rubble in which to build their nests, the largemouth does not mind using mud. Bass may be fighters, but the males are surely a henpecked lot! They do all the work building the nests, while the females stay out in deep water. The nest, generally found along the shore in one to twelve feet of water, is a circular area about 1½ to 2 times the length of the bass, which the male sweeps clean with his tail. When finished, he stands guard until the female arrives to lay her eggs. A smallmouth female can lay about 8,000 eggs per pound of body weight. The sticky eggs fall to the bottom. Then the female leaves for good while the male not only stands guard against predators night and day, but keeps the eggs aerated and clear of debris with constant movements of the fins.

241

What the weather is like around a particular lake during several crucial days in May or June may have a tremendous influence on the quality of bass fishing that lake will produce three or four years hence. Severe temperature fluctuations may kill a large per cent of the eggs or newly hatched fry for a particular year, and four years later fishermen will wonder what happened to the bass fishing.

Under suitable temperature conditions the eggs will hatch in 3 to 4 days, the transparent young remaining on the bottom several more days, finally to rise as a swarm of black fry — generally 7 to 14 days from the time the eggs were laid. All this time the good old faithful father bass remains on guard until the young ones finally disperse. This may last about a week for the smallmouth bass, and longer for the largemouths. Of course, the latter may finally hurry things along by eating a few. For the next several months the baby bass will feed on tiny water organisms, particularly water fleas. As they grow older their diet will gradually change. By the time they are grown they will prefer crayfish, frogs, other fish, and various kinds of insects. At the end of the first summer the bass will be about three inches long. During this time, the black stripe running the length of the body will distinguish the largemouth from the smallmouth, whose tail will have a pronounced vertical bar on the end of it. By the end of the second year the growing bass will average about six inches and about nine inches the third year. In fact, the males will have matured by that time. Females will generally have reached maturity when they are about eleven inches.

For many years it was supposed that bass were best managed through various restrictions as to size of bass taken, time of year, and method of taking them. In recent years most states have liberalized their bass fishing laws on the assumption that the best thing a fisherman can do to conserve warm water fishes is to take a sensible harvest. It is now known that although a multitude of bass are born each year, about one-half of all bass in a lake die each year, regardless of whether a lake is fished or not. In fact, so inefficient are fishermen in their harvest that studies have shown that in the average pond only about 11% of largemouths and 13% of smallmouths are ever caught by them. The logical answer is that bass regulations should be liberalized to permit fishermen the opportunity to double or triple their annual harvest.

Flounders

One of the important groups of marine fishes, both from a commercial and a sport fisheries standpoint, is the flatfish tribe to which belong such species as the various flounders, soles, hog choker, dabs, witch and halibut. As a commercial fisheries this group has in recent years been yielding about 80 million pounds a year in the North Atlantic. Most of them are taken with otter trawls. Anglers use hand lines to light rods and reels with from one to three hooks attached close to the sinker. Bait generally consists of sea worms or clams.

One of nature's most baffling phenomena occurs with this group of fishes. The various species start life resembling the fry of any other fish. Then, when they are about three-quarters of an inch long, one of the eyes begins to migrate over the head to a position adjacent to the other eye, and the fish begins to live on its side with both eyes staring upward. What eye migrates all depends on the species of fish involved. In the case of the Summer Flounder or Fluke, for instance, the right eye always moves over to live with the left eye. Since the mouth retains somewhat its original position, the fish looks as if its mouth opens sideways. The fluke's talent does not end here, however, for it is able to simulate the pattern and color of the bottom on which the flounder spends most of its time.

This fish is found off the Atlantic Coast from New Brunswick to South Carolina but chiefly off the southern New England and New York coastline. Many are annually taken along New Hampshire's coastline. In fall the fluke migrates offshore into 40 to 80 fathoms of water and returns to shallower water in spring, where fishermen pursue it from boats, piers and from the shore. The Summer Flounder ranges in weight from about $\frac{3}{4}$ of a pound up to 15 or 16 pounds — when it is often referred to as a "doormat". One of about 30 pounds was reported taken off Fishers Island about 1915.

Little is known of its breeding habits. It seems to spawn in late autumn, winter, and early spring, well offshore.

Despite what some restaurants can do to hide the fact, the flounder furnishes a food of high quality.

Walleye

We don't hear too much about walleyes in most of New Hampshire. On rare occasions one is caught in the Merrimack or Contoocook Rivers. The sportsmen who plan to do some fishing along the Connecticut River in the southwestern part of the state, or in the lower reaches of the Contoocook River, however, might do well to know a little about walleyes. They are there.

This fish belongs to the Perch family. It gets its name from the fact that the outer part of its eye has a milky or muddy appearance which gives it that wall-eyed look. Although specimens have been caught weighing twenty-two pounds and measuring three feet in length, they average about two to seven pounds in weight. This fish is found both in large streams and in lakes, but it prefers large clear water lakes with clean hard bottoms.

The males begin to mature during their second year when about twelve inches long, while the females mature their third year when about thirteen inches in length. Spawning season begins shortly after the ice melts and when water temperatures reach 45°–50° F. Usually a large female, accompanied by several smaller sized males, comes into shallow water — generally at night — where one can often hear them splashing about. The eggs — 23,000 to 50,000 per pound of fish — are scattered at random over sand bars, rocky reefs, or gravel. After spawning, the adults return to deep water and leave the eggs untended. Incubation of the eggs takes about twelve to eighteen days, depending on water temperatures.

At first the young live mainly on microscopic water organisms and tiny insects. When they are about two inches long they begin to add fish to their diet. The adults eat great quantities of fish, particularly yellow perch, and also crayfish, frogs, and snails. They generally feed in schools.

The best fishing for walleyes is from the latter part of May through June, and the middle of September through October. Although they can be caught in mid-day by trolling deep, they are most vulnerable during twilight hours when they come into shallow water to feed. At such times they can be taken with fly, spinning, or casting rods. Their flesh is firm, white and delicious.

245

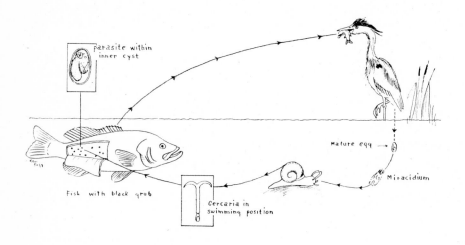

parasite within
inner cyst

Fish with black grub

Cercaria in
swimming position

Mature egg

Miracidium

Parasites in Fish

Every year the Management and Research Division of the New Hampshire Fish and Game Department receives many inquiries concerning various parasites found in or on different fish species. These generally involve some of the more obvious ones, such as black grubs or yellow grubs found in the skin and flesh of fish, and tape or round worms found in the intestinal tract. Few people realize how many different kinds of parasites actually live on fishes. Some idea can be gathered from reading the report of a study recently completed by Carl Sindermann in Massachusetts. In a bulletin titled *Parasites of Fishes of North Central Massachusetts,* he reports that the 581 fish examined by them contained a total of 44 different parasite species. In certain parts of the United States fish contain a tapeworm which can mature in man. Fortunately, to date no parasites have been found in New England fish which have proved to be harmful to man. So long as they are cooked even parasitized fish may be eaten with impunity.

Parasites do, however, play an important role on fish populations. When abundant they may affect fish in the following manner:

1. By stunting growth of fish.
2. By causing mortality of fish on certain occasions.
3. By causing sterility in fish.

The latter damage is considered one of the most serious problems in New Hampshire, being caused by the bass tapeworm.

A summer seldom passes in which one or more fishermen don't bring in a bass, yellow perch, sunfish, or sometimes rainbow trout, covered with raised black spots. "Black Spot", as this infection is generally called, is caused by the larval stage of several kinds of flukes (flat worms) which establish themselves immediately beneath the scales, on the fins, and sometimes in the flesh. There isn't much that can be done about this parasite in nature. When fish-eating birds such as kingfishers and herons eat a fish with "Black Spot" the grubs mature within the birds and lay their eggs, which pass out of the birds through their bill or feces. If the eggs land in a fish pond they hatch and a complicated life

cycle is started. First there develops a larval stage which enters a snail. It lives in the snail approximately 42 days and then emerges in another larval form, swimming about until it makes contact with a suitable fish, which it immediately penetrates. In about 22 days the fish develops the black spot which bothers the fisherman — and the fish.

Another fluke, one which has a life cycle very similar to the black grub, produces white or yellow cysts in the flesh of the fish — particularly yellow perch. It is not particularly appetizing to see a grub emerge from these cysts when they are squeezed.

Another fluke spends a part of its life as a grub in the eyes of fish. There are many other flukes, some of which have strange and complicated life cycles. Through long and careful research by a large number of parasitologists who have solved many of these cycles, we now have a considerable amount of information concerning some of these parasites. With this fundamental knowledge as a basis, the possibility of developing methods of control becomes more probable.

In addition to Sinderman's *Parasites of Fishes of North Central Massachusetts,* another excellent publication on the subject has recently been put out by the State of Maine, *The Larger Animal Parasites of the Fresh-Water Fishes of Maine,* written by Marvin C. Meyer.

Bass Tapeworm

Of all fish parasites found in and on our native New Hampshire fishes, none gives us more concern than the bass tapeworm. The mature form of this parasite, living in the intestines of bass, passes off eggs. If an egg is accidently eaten by a copepod (a tiny water crustacean) the first larval stage of the tapeworm is started. If this infected copepod is then eaten by a fish — any one of a number of species — another stage of the parasite develops which penetrates the walls of the intestine and encysts in the various body organs — such as the liver — and there undergoes development to a more advanced stage. Then if this infected fish is eaten by a bass, the tapeworm transforms once more to become the mature form and thus completes its life cycle.

Realizing that fish have to contend with numerous other kinds of tapeworms, why be so concerned about this particular one? The second larval stage of the parasite is the real troublemaker. Occasionally an angler will have noticed, in cleaning a fish, that the internal organs are unrecognizably matted together. Several hundred white cylindrical worms may be present in this visceral mass, and may cause such extensive damage that normal organic functions of the fish are retarded. In larger bass the sex organs are often heavily infested, thus partially or totally inhibiting reproduction. It is this damage to the reproductive capacity of bass which causes us the greatest concern.

What can we do about these various parasites in fish? Once the fish of a lake are infected, remedies are at present practically unknown. It is hoped, however, that the pond reclamation program may, in some instances, break the life cycle of various parasites to the extent that a body of water is "cleaned up". Studies are currently underway to test this theory. Extreme caution must be exercised in transferring fish from one lake to another. The well-meaning sportsmen who believes he is furthering the cause of fish management by carrying fish from one water body to another, or the thoughtless angler who blithely empties the contents of his minnow bucket into a pond, should remember that he might be starting the ruination of a good fish pond.

How Many Fish in That Pond

Have you ever stood on the shore of a pond and idly wondered how many fish it contained? In fisheries management this question is prompted by more than idle curiosity. It becomes an important part of our entire fisheries program. Not only is it desirable to have an estimate of the total population present, but of still greater importance is it to know the ratios of various species of fish to each other. The reason for this should be quite obvious. A "healthy" population of fish will have the various species in proper ratio to each other. If, for some reason or other, one species becomes so abundant that it is out of balance with the other species, a chain of detrimental reactions is set in motion which eventually reflects itself in the type of fishing that pond produces.

It is possible to get a reasonably accurate idea of the number of fish in a pond. Several methods are in general use in the country, but each employs essentially the same basic approach. First, a number of fish are netted, marked and then returned to the pond. It is then assumed that these marked fish will again mix with the other fish in the pond. There upon netting operations are continued. The ratio of the marked fish caught, thereafter, to the unmarked fish caught should approximate the ratio of all marked fish originally returned to the water and the total fish population in the pond.

If you hear a fisheries biologist mumbling something about the "Schnabel Method" or "Thompson's Method", the chances are he is trying to determine what the fish population of some pond happens to be, and he is applying the formula worked out by these men. Here in New Hampshire our men generally use a modification of the Schnabel Method as developed by Thompson.

During the past several years our fisheries biologists have carried on these operations in various ponds now under intensive management for bass.

In the fall of 1955 for instance, biologist Arthur Riel estimated that there were approximately 1,555 bass in Crooked Pond in Loudon. Since a simple explanation of his procedure is impossible, let us examine the process step by step. The following table shows the results of six days of netting in the pond.

Date	Sample Number	A	M	B	AB	≦ AB	C	≦C	P
Sept. 19	1	566	566	—	—	—	—	—	—
Sept. 20	2	270	184	566	152,820	152,820	86	86	1,777
Sept. 21	3	86	37	750	64,500	217,320	49	135	1,610
Sept. 22	4	46	21	787	36,202	253,522	25	160	1,585
Sept. 23	5	21	7	808	16,968	270,490	14	174	1,555
Sept. 26	6	78	33	815	63,570	334,060	45	219	1,525

The formula used in the determination of the estimated population was:

$$P = \frac{\Sigma AB}{\Sigma C}$$

A equals number of fish caught on any given date.
M equals number of fish marked and returned.
B equals number of marked fish present on any date.
AB equals "A" multiplied by "B".
≦ AB equals the sum of all products (AB) calculated to date.
C equals the number of returns on any date.
≦ C equals the sum of all returns to date.
P equals the estimated population on any date.

Thus, on September 19, 566 bass were caught, marked and returned. On September 20, 270 bass were caught of which 184 were marked ones recaptured. These were then returned while the 86 unmarked bass were also marked and returned. By applying the above formula it was estimated that there were 1,777 bass. Since his first sampling was obviously still too small, Riel continued the netting operations until his last three estimates were fairly consistent. This happened on his fourth, fifth, and sixth days of netting. Taking the average of 1,585, 1,555, and 1,523 he estimated a total of 1,555 bass for Crooked Pond.

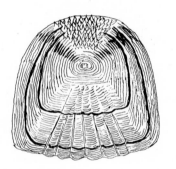

Fish Scales Tell

Why do fisheries biologists spend so much time with fish scales? The research crew of New Hampshire's Fish and Game Department has beeen carrying on a concentrated collection of scales from specific study areas and analyzing the data obtained from them. Fish scales act as the fishes' autobiography and few humans keep a more accurate diary of their living conditions.

Fish are born without scales. Some, like horned pout, never develop scales, but most do. Sometime during the first year of its life — varying with different species — the growing fry develops scale nuclei under its skin, set there like shingles on a roof. The greater part of these "shingles" will always remain imbedded in the skin with only a small portion showing. As the fish grows these scale nuclei begin to grow by adding rings of new material around the edge of the scale. By the time winter sets in there will be a number of these growth rings. Over the winter months the fish eats less, growth slows down, and consequently the growth rings on the scale become crowded together. The following spring when the fish finds and eats more food, these scale circles are again laid farther apart. The crowded growth circles which developed during winter are called an "annulus" and it is these which tell us the age of the fish.

But an expert at reading fish scales can find much more on them than just the age of the fish. Many fish give up eating for a time while they spawn. This will show up between the annuli and tell the fisheries man at what year the fish started spawning. Scales of ocean fish, like salmon, which come to fresh water to spawn will show a very noticeable difference in their growth rings the year the fish left salt water. An expert fish scale reader can even tell from the scales alone whether fish from one pond have grown better than fish from another pond and at what year of their life they grew the fastest.

Since the scale grows at the same rate as the fish, it is possible to take fish before they have spawned, measure them, then measure the total scale and the distance between the annuli. By simple ratios it is then possible to back-calculate and determine what length the fish was at the end of each year.

All of this must have some practical value if it is to do our fisheries work any good.

What are some of the practical aspects of fish scale studies?

First of all a little should be known about the term "Condition Factor". Some years ago one of America's better known fisheries biologists developed a formula by which to compare the condition of important game fish species from one pond to another. It is called the C (or condition) Factor formula and is as follows: $100,000 \times \text{weight} \div \text{length}^3$. Without going into a more detailed explanation on how this formula was developed, let us see how it is being applied to New Hampshire's problems.

Several years ago the Fish and Game Department developed several largemouth bass ponds. One pond, which had been reclaimed and then stocked with fingerling bass and crayfish, produced a good population of bass but most of them seemed to be skinny. Scale samples were taken from a representative number of bass, which were measured and weighed. These scales were then read to determine the age of the bass. It was found that they were in their third growing season, weighed an average of 4.43 ounces, and averaged 8.73 inches in length. From these data biologists were able to determine that their C Factor was 42.1. In the meantime the Department has been, and is in the process of, getting data on the C Factor of bass in numerous other New Hampshire waters. On the basis of data from other lakes and ponds biologists' suspicions were confirmed that fish from the pond in question were in poor condition.

Next the cause had to be determined. Scales from these fish were again put under the microscope and back calculations were made of their three-years' growth. These showed the bass grew well the first two years but poorly the third year. This indicated that the pond in question is a fertile one with a good plankton growth to take care of growing fingerling bass, but that there is a lack of food for the adult bass. This was verified when Department personnel went back to the pond and through careful trapping operations found that the crayfish planted there had not survived. A heavy stocking of alewives was then made to correct this situation, with the outcome still to be determined.

Sometimes back calculations of growth on scales will plainly show how bass or trout grew poorly while fingerlings, but rapidly once they became adults. In that case an entirely different remedy is required. The point of this story is that "scales tell a lot".

INVERTEBRATES

Lobster

The American Lobster is found only on the eastern coast of North America. The most northern point at which lobsters have been taken is Henley Harbor in Labrador. The most southern point has been North Carolina. Between these two points lobsters are found in a belt about 30 to 50 miles wide, although off Cape Cod this belt broadens to nearly 200 miles on George's Bank. They inhabit depths from one to more than 100 fathoms. In the fall they move into deeper water and toward shore in April and May. The average total length of lobsters taken for market is from 9 to 10 inches, but these crustaceans can become considerably larger. A 45-pounder was taken off the Virginia Capes in 1935.

The lobster's skeleton is on the outside and must be shed every time he outgrows it. The first molt begins between the second and fifth day after hatching and is repeated throughout life. True characteristics of an adult lobster are not attained until the fourth molt. The size at which the female reaches sexual maturity varies in different areas. In New Hampshire the average size at maturity is 11½ inches or more. Mating occurs in summer during the molting season, while actual spawning takes place the following spring. Eggs are laid every two years. To spawn the female turns on her back and flexes her abdomen into a pocket. As she lays the eggs they flow into the pocket and in the process are fertilized from sperm obtained from the male summer before. An 8-inch lobster produces about 5,000 eggs while a 15-incher may lay as many as 97,000. The eggs stick to the abdominal appendages or swimmerets, where it takes them about 10 to 11 months to hatch.

Lobster fishery in New England has shown a general decline since 1889 when 30,500,000 pounds were marketed. By 1940 this had declined to about 11,000,000 pounds. Intensive studies are now underway to determine how to counteract this decline. The most important conservation measure at present is the protection of egg-bearing females, and minimum size laws designed to allow small lobsters to escape the fishery.

Fishery Leaflet 74, *The American Lobster,* put out by the U. S. Fish and Wildlife Service, contains much valuable information for those interested in this gourmet's delight from New Hampshire's coastline.

Crayfishes

If anyone has ever made a study of the crayfishes in New Hampshire, we do not know about it. In fact, we don't even know how may different kinds there are in our state, although we have found at least three different species here and there are probably more.

All are most active at night when they roam about looking for food. They eat a large variety of things, such as algae, decaying plants and animals, and any small animals they can catch. They are good scavengers. They also have many enemies, such as raccoons, frogs, birds, fish, turtles, and snakes. People often ask us whether crayfish are good to eat. They are, but they should be cooked well because they harbor many kinds of parasites.

Like lobsters crayfish must shed their outer shell from time to time so that they can grow; in fact this may happen eight or more times the first year of life, but less often in the adult. When the time comes to moult, the shell splits on the upper side and the animal withdraws its entire body through the opening. Immediately after moulting, the crawfish has a soft shell. This hardens after a few days. During the winter growth slows down and no moulting is necessary. When spring comes the male moults but the female must wait for about three weeks until her young have hatched and the young have left her.

Mating habits are unusual. In late summer and autumn the male passes sperm into a pocket in the lower side of the female, where it is kept until she is ready to lay her eggs. Some lay them in autumn and others not until spring. When laying time comes the female turns on her back and may lay anywhere from sixty to several hundred eggs. As they are extruded, the sperm she has been storing in her pocket all these weeks is released to fertilize the eggs. At the same time a sticky substance attaches them to the female's swimmerets where they are carried about and aerated until they hatch in spring. The newly hatched crayfish cling to their mother about two weeks before they leave to fend for themselves.

The New Hampshire Fish and Game Department is taking an increased interest in the crayfishes because of their importance as forage for fish.

Oysters

While some people retch at the sight of oysters, others gulp them raw, in stews, fried, or baked, and consider them one of the great delicacies of the culinary cuisine. One adult oyster might liberate as many as half-a-billion eggs into the water during one spawning season. Unfortunately, many animals besides man like to eat oysters. Drill-borers, starfish, quarter-ducks rayfish, drums, oyster leeches, boring clams, crabs, red copepods, ghost shrimps, and ducks all take their share, to the extent that by the end of a season only one or two adult oysters are left of the millions of eggs shed by one female.

Let's follow the development of this mollusk from egg to oyster-on-the-half-shell. First of all, remember that while the sexes are separate, both males and females may change sex from one year to the next. Most oysters are males during their first year, but gradually a 50-50 sex ratio is established. The eastern oyster, found along the Atlantic Coast, breeds during the summer, generally when the temperature of the water goes above 65°F. Shortly after eggs are released they become fertilized in the water. As they grow they form mulberry-like balls of cells with hair-like projections which cause movement. After about thirty hours they develop into organisms about 1/400 of an inch in length with two similar minute shells. Within another three or four days these larvae grow into so-called umbo stage larvae in which the two shells — unlike clams, for instance — are different in shape. In this form they drift about in the currents for about eight or ten days when they "strike" or become attached to clean shells, rocks, or other hard objects. They are then known as "spats". They reach a marketable length of three to four inches in about three to five years, depending on the water temperature.

Oysters are found along both the Pacific and the Atlantic Coast. Three species are utilized on the Pacific Coast: the small native Olympia oyster, the introduced eastern oyster, and the Pacific or Japanese oyster brought in from Japan in 1902. The last one is now the most important commercially. On the Atlantic Coast the eastern oyster grows naturally or is cultivated in every seaboard state, including our Great Bay and coastal waters.

Old-wives tales to the contrary, oysters may be eaten every month of the year. They may be thin and watery after spawning.

Fresh-Water Clams

It is difficult to imagine a fresh-water clam (or mussel) as living anything but a very prosaic existence. However, there is more about clams than meets the eye. We know, of course, that all of them must live in water. They are most abundant in large rivers. There are many different kinds and shapes, ranging in size from about twice the size of a pin head to as much as eleven inches in length. They get along without a head or eyes. If you want to know what is the front part of the clam, watch for his big muscular axe-shaped foot which is pushed out of the bivalve shells in front and used to hunch the clam along, some as fast as several feet per hour. Most of the time, however, the clam just lies there sucking in and pumping out water through siphons which protrude toward the rear. As the water goes in, it goes through a screening process to extract the plankton and organic detritus which serve as food for the clams.

The love life of clams becomes a little confusing, since clams don't all follow the same routine. As a whole, it falls into two major patterns. One large group of clams is hermaphroditic (an individual being both male and female). In this group the eggs attach, are fertilized and develop on the clam's gills, and here one might find anywhere from 1 to 20 young in various stages of development. Although reproduction probably occurs throughout the year, very few are "born" during the winter. When released into the water, the immature individuals are fully formed, some being almost one-third as large as the adult.

Another group of clams consists of males and females. During reproduction the sperm from a male enters the water and then into a nearby female to fertilize the eggs. The mother clam retains the developing embryos only during the early stages of their development. There may be anywhere from several thousand embryos in smaller species to 3,000,000 in some large species. Some species of clams are gravid between April and August, while some carry their young from midsummer to the following summer. When these are released into the water they are free-swimming larvae, have a superficial resemblance to the adults and are called "glochidium". Now occurs one of the crucial moments in their life, and this is probably the reason so many young ones are produced at a time.

Unless a fish brushes against them within a few days, they are doomed. Should a fish come within reaching distance of these baby clams, they grab on for dear life — on the gills, fins, or general body surface — where they become little parasites. Some clams must have a definite species of fish on which to attach, while other species of clams are less particular, so long as it's a fish. Once on the fish, tissue grows over the clams.

This parasitic stage usually lasts ten to thirty days, although much longer for some. During this time the larva takes on the adult appearance. Finally it breaks out of the enveloping tissue, falls to the bottom of the lake or stream where it lives its next one to eight years (depending on the species) as a juvenile clam before growing to adulthood.

Even if fresh-water clams are not as palatable as their cousins from the ocean they are, as a whole, useful. Many animals — fish, birds, reptiles, mammals such as raccoons and muskrats — thrive on them. An entire industry — pearl buttons — is provided by clams. And of course, from time to time a piece of debris or sand may lodge in a clam where it becomes irritating. To counteract it, the clam begins to secrete a substance around it which can eventually end up around the neck of a fair damsel as a pearl.

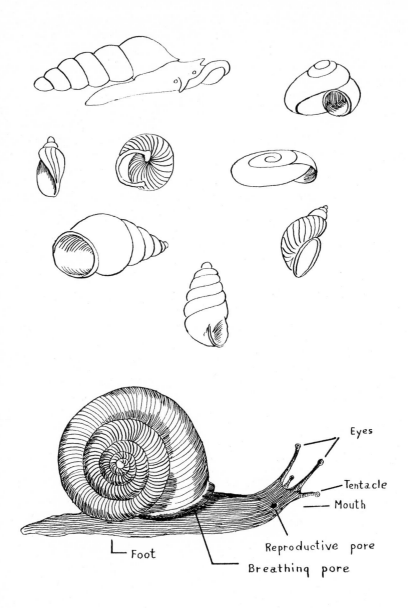

Eyes

Tentacle

Mouth

Foot

Reproductive pore

Breathing pore

Snails

Snails are everywhere — under logs and boards, in leaf mold, in lakes and streams, in and adjacent to the ocean, in gardens and, too often, in the middle of lettuce heads. Snail shells are of many kinds, shapes, and colors. Some spend all their time on land, while others live in water.

Snails have an interesting anatomy, with variations in the different kinds. A typical example of a land form is the common white-lipped snail, easily recognizable because of the white margin on the shell. This snail is usually found in the leaf mold of woods and forests. Just under the edge of the shell on the right hand side is a small opening in the snail's body through which it breathes. On its head are four projections which look like coarse feelers. In fact, the shorter pair are feelers. The pair of longer ones act as periscopes, since the snail's eyes are placed on the end of them. On the underside of the head is the mouth. Near the mouth is a gland from which comes the slime the snail uses to make the track on which it moves. Not all snails are built this way. There are pond snails, for instance, that have but one pair of feelers, and whose eyes are located at the base of these feelers. Most of the snail's body consists of the "foot".

An interesting feature about snails is that they are hermaphrodites; namely, both male and female. Despite this fact, snails generally crossbreed. The several to about 40 eggs of the white-lipped snail are laid through an opening immediately behind the right feeler. Eggs of land snails are shell-covered, often looking like small pearls. They are laid in moist places away from sunlight. The young hatch in from 20 to 30 days, closely resembling the parents. In about two years they mature. Some land snails do not lay eggs, since these develop within the body and the young are then born. Pond snails lay eggs in little masses of jelly, each kind producing eggs of a definite type. In some the jelly is yellow, in others clear; some with flat egg masses, while others thick. Their eggs are not covered with shells.

In water snails can let themselves down from one plant to another on a thread of slime or make little rafts of slime that float on water. From the human's point of view snails play an important role. Many are hosts to deadly human diseases and parasites; others are damaging to crops. Many are highly important food.

Bryozoa

Have you ever looked in a pond and observed a jelly-like mass anywhere from the size of a grapefruit to that of a bushel basket? These translucent masses, speckled with brownish-colored polka dots, are generally attached to sticks or logs and you may have thought you were looking at fish or frog eggs. As a matter of fact, you were looking at a colony of thousands of animals called *bryozoa* or *moss animalcules*.

The individual bryozoans are located on the outside of the jelly. The jelly-like stuff which is secreted by the animals is clear until it becomes discolored by algae and bacteria. Each tiny white spot on the jelly beneath the water consists of a hundred or more individual animals. As the colonies become large in the latter part of summer, they are apt to trap gas bubbles and float to the surface. The portions of the colonies exposed to air are killed. The jelly is pushed up in places by the bubbles and dries out to form dome-shaped shells.

When bryozoans are touched they give off slime, but they are harmless. The individual bryozoan, when viewed under a microscope, is a little tubular affair topped by a plume of moving tentacles. These threadlike tentacles sweep microscopic food particles into the mouth of the bryozoan. Should the animal be irritated it will simply withdraw into a leathery sheath. After a few moments, however, the graceful tentacles will again blossom forth.

A peculiarity about bryozoans is their method of reproduction. It has two systems. As the colony increases in size the individuals simply reproduce by budding like a plant. During a certain period of the summer, however, small portions of the bryozoans are set aside in flat packages called "statoblasts". As these are freed they drift away, often in such large numbers that they form windrows along lake shores. The edges of these tiny packages have hooked spines which help them catch free rides on moving objects. Like seeds, they can overwinter and start new colonies of bryozoans the following spring.

Although there are about 3500 different kinds of bryozoa, most of them are found in salt water, only about 40 kinds being freshwater species. Of these, 14 species have been reported from America.

Fresh-Water Sponges

Few people realize that fresh-water sponges exist and that they can be found in New Hampshire waters. In looking for fresh-water sponges one should not expect to find them resembling in appearance the sponges used to wash the car, for these are exclusively of marine origin. However, as regards their biology, fresh-water and marine sponges are essentially alike.

Sponges vary greatly in form and appearance but are basically composed of a silica framework, having a delicate tissue covering interspersed with pores which are connected with a network of internal canals. Through these pores microscopic food particles are sucked in and traverse the canals. The activity of the sponge cannot be seen with the naked eye and is even difficult to view under the microscope. Reproduction is usually accomplished by the germination of many seed-like bodies called gemmules, which survive the rigors of winter or the killing summer temperatures and give rise to new sponges. It is these tiny gemmules which allow for the wide distribution of sponges.

In searching for sponges one should look on the underside of submerged logs or sticks in gently moving waters. They present the appearance of green or greenish-brown growths on the logs, and when picked up have a sandpapery feeling and a characteristic odor when crushed between the fingers.

The assigning of a correct species name to a sponge calls for the services of a specialist, for many of them are differentiated by the appearance and structure of the minute silica rods making up the skeleton.

Sponges are extremely old in origin, many fossil species having been uncovered. Today there are roughly three thousand living species of sponge known, including both fresh-water and marine forms.

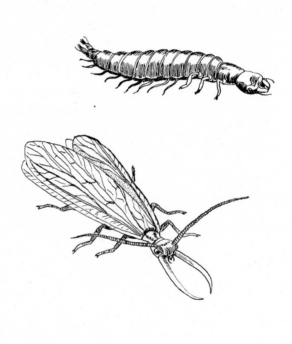

Hellgrammite

Most fishermen in New Hampshire know that a hellgrammite is an excellent bass bait. Few people would probably associate this insect with the chalky white egg masses, about the size of a 25¢ piece, generally found on piers, masonry work or stones overhanging streams. The two thousand or more minute larvae hatch in about two weeks after the eggs have been laid and go for water as rapidly as possible to live under stones in riffles. Here they live and grow for about three years, anchoring themselves to the bottom with hooks protruding from their rear end. They feed on naiads of stone-flies, May-flies, and on other insects.

A full grown hellgrammite attains a length of about three inches. They have powerful jaws, are fiercely predaceous, and so ill-natured that they will seize at anything disturbing them.

Toward the end of their second year they crawl out of the water, hide under a nearby log or stone to pupate, emerging in about ten days as a large handsome fly about four inches in length having long pincers and known in New Hampshire as Dobson-flies. These are short-lived, generally flying about at night mating and seeking a place to lay their eggs.

Hellgrammites are best collected in fast flowing streams by holding a mesh screen in the swiftest part of riffles while a companion turns over stones immediately upstream from the net. These larvae will live for several weeks if kept in a shaded, cool, well-vented container full of moist grass.

A good bass man will treat a Dobson Fly with utmost respect, for there goes a potential two thousand hellgrammites or bass baits.

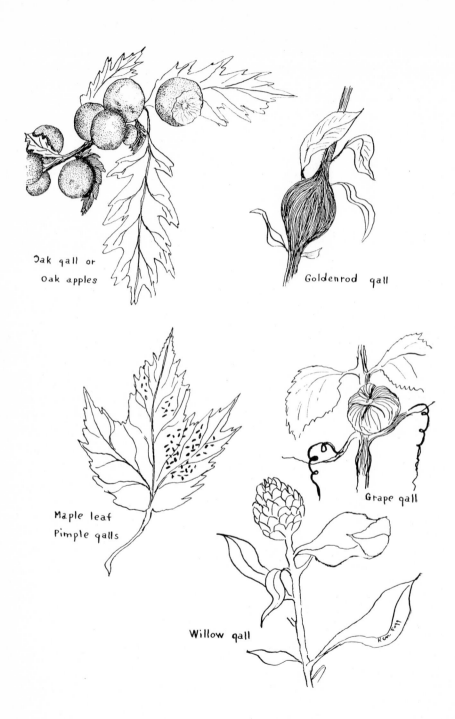

Oak gall or
Oak apples

Goldenrod gall

Maple leaf
Pimple galls

Grape gall

Willow gall

Galls

Any boy who has strolled through the woods will at one time or another have wondered about certain strange growths found on various plants. Well he might, for these so-called "galls" are one of the baffling mysteries of nature. These growths are found on a large variety of plants. Some of the more commonly observed galls are: the smooth round or oblong swellings on the stems of goldenrods; the round and leathery so-called oak-apples found on the leaves and stems of oak trees, which boys like to step on to see if they will pop; the "pimple galls", those red little protuberances one often finds crowded on the bottom of red maple leaves; or the gall that looks like a pine or spruce cone growing on the end of a willow branch. These are but a few examples of a great many kinds of insect galls which may be found in an immense variety of shapes and sizes on practically every part of a tree or plant from roots to the tips of leaves.

There are some things biologists know about galls, but much more they don't know. It is known, for instance, that galls are created by insects such as plant lice, flies, moths, beetles, or mites, but most often by one group known technically as Cynipids — commonly called gall-flies or gall-wasps. The remarkable thing about this is the fact that each species of gall-creating insects infests a special part of one or more particular species of plants, be it leaf or stem or root, and the gall produced by each species of insect is always the same form. Hence, when you see the spindle-shaped swelling on the stem of a goldenrod you may be certain it was produced by a tiny species of moth. What really baffles the naturalist is the method by which these galls are produced. It has been supposed that at the time the insect lays its egg there is deposited in the tissue of the plant a drop of poison which causes the abnormal growth. But why should each insect deposit a poison which develops a different type of growth? Furthermore, in the case of many species of insects the gall does not develop until the larva is hatched. When the larva begins to feed the abnormal growth of the plant commences. Mystery or not, gall insects get off to a cozy start inside a house that grows from a drop of poison.

American Insect Galls by Millett Taylor Thompson has a set of photographs of galls which can help anyone inquisitive about these strange growths to identify many of the more common ones.

PRINCIPLES AND
PHENOMENA OF NATURE

Autumn Foliage

Every autumn many thousands of tourists travel the highways and byways of New Hampshire to view with awe an amazing pageant — the colorful death scene of the year's foliage. With mountains and valleys as backdrop, no man-made spectacle can equal it. To understand how the stagehands prepare the scenes, let us go back to the beginning of summer, when trees are covered with green leaves.

The primary function of leaves is to manufacture food for the tree. Each leaf is made up of hundreds of thousands of microscopic living cells containing various complex chemicals. One of these is an amazing green chemical called chlorophyll which gives leaves their green color. It is one of the only things known to man which, with the help of light, turns water and carbon dioxide into sugar — the food utilized by plants. There are also yellow and brown chemicals in the cells of green leaves. The food each leaf manufactures during summer would do the tree little good if it were not for tiny tubes leading through the leaf stem into the branches. These tubes carry materials to the leaf to replenish the chlorophyll as it is used up and to carry the food into the tree. At the base of the leaf stem is a tiny furrow which acts as a cutoff valve in fall. When this "valve" begins to shut off late in summer, less and less chlorophyll reaches the leaf. Consequently, as this green material is used up faster than it is brought in, the yellow and brown chemicals in the leaf begin to show up. This is particularly noticeable in birches and elms.

Meanwhile, the clogged tubes are also cutting down the amount of sugar which can flow out of the leaf into the tree. It begins to pile up in the leaves, forming a new substance. That's what produces the pink to purple colors. All depends on whether the liquid in the leaf cells is acid or alkaline. Sumacs and red maples have an acid liquid so their leaves turn various colors of red. Ash and dogwoods have an alkaline liquid so their leaves turn blue to purple. While frost may help to hurry the process along, don't let anyone tell you that it causes the autumn colors.

In the meantime, the shut-off valve closes entirely. Finally, there comes a day with a little breeze and the leaf, having completed its function in life, drifts earthward where it becomes again part of the soil to send nourishment into trees to grow new leaves.

Poison Ivy

Adding its bit to autumn's blaze of glory in New Hampshire is a vine along stone walls and on trunks of trees, or simply a small plant tucked unobtrusively among the other plants, whose charming colors in autumn will not erase from many a memory the misery it can cause.

Poison ivy is common enough in New Hampshire so that people roaming our fields and forests must forever remain on guard against it. Almost everyone starts life immune to poison ivy. Some people have been able to come in contact with this plant for many years before they finally developed the characteristic blisters and itching, while others become sensitive to its poison early in life. Once a person has become sensitized he will be much more susceptible to poison ivy thereafter.

What is it in the poison ivy plant that causes all the trouble? It is a fluid called oleoresin contained in the leaflets, stems of the leaves, twigs and bark. Light contact with the plant will not liberate the poisonous juice. The plant must be bruised. On the other hand, so stable is this poisonous chemical that soot particles from the burning plant can infect sensitive people. Even dead and dried-out plants are infectious.

Some people claim they are so sensitive to poison ivy that they catch it every summer from the pollen. This is not true. Their best bet is to keep the dog or cat away from poison ivy. These pets can easily carry the poison on their coats and then infect people who pet them.

One to two days after exposure the person who is sensitive to this plant will generally show the usual skin reaction — reddening, then itching followed by blisters. Contrary to popular belief, the fluid from these blisters does not help spread the itching to uninfected areas.

Animal Migrations

As autumn approaches we become aware of the seasonal migration of birds. Webster's Dictionary states that migration means "to pass periodically from one region or climate to another for feeding or breeding, as various birds and animals". Actually, migration is a phenomenon of vast proportions. It is, of course, not restricted to birds; although theirs is the most spectacular. Various species of fish migrate regularly. One example is the annual run of salmon and shad from the ocean into and up fresh-water streams to spawn. Still more spectacular is that of the eels, which spend a lifetime in fresh water and finally migrate thousands of miles to spawn and die in the Sargasso Sea.

Among the mammals there are the blind wanderings of Lemmings, those little Arctic animals that periodically march to their destruction in the sea. Bats participate in north and southward movements. Leaving the males in the North Pacific and the Antarctic Ocean, the females and young of the fur seals annually migrate almost to subtropical waters. Great numbers of squirrels periodically start a cross-country movement. Among the insect world the Monarch or Milkweed Butterflies are well known for their mass flights to the south each fall.

Birds exhibit many types of migrations. As a rule these consist of a movement to the breeding grounds in the spring and to the wintering grounds in the fall. Even here there are exceptions to the rule. For instance, from time to time northern states are invaded by large numbers of Snowy Owls from the north. This probably happens during years when hares and smaller rodents decrease to such an extent that these owls must seek new feeding grounds. Late each summer people in northern states are apt to witness a migration in reverse. This happens when the young of certain species of herons make a leisurely trip northward shortly after they have learned to fly and prior to the time they head south for the winter.

Even the normal spring and fall migrations of birds manifest themselves in a variety of types. Some birds, like the English Sparrow and ruffed grouse, shift from nesting to winter cover and back but may spend their entire life within a mile of their birthplace. There are species such as the bluejay and crow where some individuals may remain in the same locality all year round, while others move southward in fall and return in spring.

Then there are the regular migrants with all their idiosyncrasies of movement. Some, like robins and blackbirds, migrate during the day while others, like orioles, tanagers, and warblers migrate overnight. In spring, robins come northward in a leisurely fashion, it taking some more than two months after leaving their winter quarters before they reach the locality where they plan to nest. On the other hand, there are birds such as the blue goose which may stay in the south until late in spring. When they finally start northward they move rapidly, almost nonstop to northern Canada. Here they may rest and court for a period of time before completing their final flight to the nesting grounds.

There is considerable variation in the distance different species, and even individuals of the same species, annually migrate. Some Black Ducks, for instance, may winter just south of the ice, wherever ponds are not frozen over, and then move but a short distance north to nest. Others may move from New Jersey to northern Quebec. Some species annually make long journeys. Nighthawks and barn swallows, for instance, push right across the equator and spend the winter months in South America. The champion globetrotter is the Arctic Tern, travelling from the Arctic to the Antarctic.

How high do birds travel when migrating? In general, it is below 3,000 feet, while many species travel only a few feet above ground. How they find their way is a guess. *The Migration of North American Birds* by Frederick C. Lincoln is a good reference for anyone interested in the whole subject of migration.

Hibernation

Hibernation may be defined as a resting state during which animals exist in a more or less dormant condition. Some of the characteristics of hibernation are: lowered metabolism, lowered respiration and heart beat, temperature approaching that of the environment, no intake of food, loss of weight and usually water. Throughout the animal kingdom there are hibernators, such as insects, protozoa, frogs and toads, earthworms, clams and snails, in addition to certain mammals — to mention just a few.

While various species have hibernation periods that vary in length and date, in general it can be said that in this region the period extends from late October or mid-November to the latter part of March or early April. Temperature and food supplies seem to be the controlling factors in bringing about hibernation, and most of the higher animals fortify themselves with a good supply of fat before entering the dormant period.

Hibernating animals seek a multitude of places in which to spend the inactive period. The one-celled protozoa encyst themselves, while frogs burrow into the mud of a pond and the toad seeks a niche below the frost line in the ground. Insects may create a cocoon or burrow into the stem of a plant or under the bark of a tree. Bears, raccoons, skunks, and squirrels are not "true" hibernators, as a mild spell during the winter months will find them venturing about. Such animals as the woodchuck and the jumping mouse are, on the other hand, hibernators in the true sense of the word. Temperature again seems to govern the spring emergence, for food is often at a premium and little is eaten by some animals when they first come out in the spring.

Predators and Predation

Webster's Dictionary defines a predatory animal as one that lives by preying upon animals; or one that is destructive or damaging to crops, buildings, etc., by consuming them. Actually, the word predator has come to mean so many different things to so many different people that Webster's definition has become totally inadequate.

Most of us are apt to consider a predator any creature that has beaten us to another creature we wanted for ourselves. If a bobcat kills a deer, a fox a rabbit, an owl a pheasant, a merganser a trout, or a snapping turtle a duck, we wonder how anyone could deny that bobcats, foxes, owls, mergansers, and turtles are predators? But then, there is always somebody who can't let well enough alone. He begins to ask questions. He wants to know whether we ourselves are predators because we kill and eat deer before the bobcat can get one. Or are deer predators because they feed on apple buds the orchardist needed to grow apples; is the fox a predator when it eats a weasel that kills rabbits; or are mergansers predators when they devour fallfish which crowd out trout?

So we stick to our guns and say that most of these animals are predators, but concede that they also do some good. We watch a loon on a remote pond that has just been stocked with $2,000 worth of trout and wince every time the loon dives and comes up with one of those precious fish — trout which could give us so much more pleasure if they were on the other end of our rod. Then we are sure this bird is a predator. At sunset, however, the loon calls; and the man from the city who does not fish but has come to enjoy New Hampshire's wilderness exclaims, "Hearing that bird was worth the entire cost of my trip." Is that loon a predator or a necessary part of our wilderness? So we waver, wondering who was wrong, the man who planted high priced fish in a remote pond, or the loon that eats fish when and where it finds them . . . because God made it that way. When thirty pheasants are liberated in a field that has enough food and cover to hold ten, and owls and foxes eat twenty of the surplus pheasants, who committed a blunder? If a state passes a buck law permitting deer to become so numerous that they would quickly destroy their own habitat if bobcats did not help to thin down their numbers, should the bobcat be commended or persecuted?

Perhaps one way to determine what is and what is not a predator would be to set up a ledger. Under assets we would list all the good things about a particular species, and under the liability column all the destructive things. If the latter column is longer, we would consider the species detrimental. So, we start with bear and immediately run into difficulties. Like the humans, there are bad bears and good bears. While most bears are fairly harmless, offer excellent sport to many hunters, and are a thrilling sight to the man fortunate enough to see one in the wild, there is the infrequent bear that has learned to kill livestock or to raid bee hives. Should our liability column state that bears kill livestock simply because an occasional individual develops the habit?

Let us forget bear for the time being and work with blue herons. Under our liability column we begin to list such items as: 1) eats trout, bass, and other game fish; 2) helps to spread fish parasites; 3) competes with game fish by eating crayfish and other important forage foods.

Under assets we list: 1) eats rough fish that compete for food with game fish; 2) helps to keep bass and other warm water game fish thinned down so that the remainder grow better; 3) is admired by many bird lovers.

As we tabulate the various factors it begins to dawn on us that our list will not work because we cannot generalize. All will depend on where the individual heron happens to be. If he is in a cut-off along the Merrimack River, he is bound to do more good than harm. On the other hand, if he is in the Merrimack Trout Rearing Station pools, he is bound to do more harm than good!

What, then, is the answer to the "predator" problem? We have seen that one man may believe an animal to be a competitor while another considers it a thing of beauty. An animal may be destructive and still essential to the balance of nature. A species may be beneficial as a whole, while certain individuals become detrimental. The thoughtful man will take these many facts into consideration before he condemns any creature. Finally, perhaps the word "predator" should be eliminated from our vocabulary, since in the final analysis the word is meaningless.

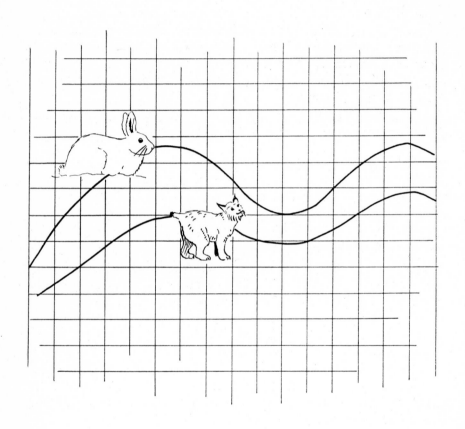

Cycles

There remain many unsolved problems and mysteries in the field of wildlife conservation. One of the most baffling is the periodic fluctuation of wildlife populations, commonly called "cycles". A mysterious catastrophe sweeps across the land killing off millions upon millions of wild creatures. Trappers in Canada have long been aware of these ups and downs of animal numbers. The fur records of the Hudson's Bay Company, which extend back for more than 250 years, were plotted on a graph. The lines were seen to rise and fall over an approximate ten-year period with surprising regularity.

These so-called "cycles" seem mainly to effect three major groups of animals: rodents, their predators, and various gallinaceous birds such as grouse and certain partridges. They are most pronounced in the far north, primarily in Canada, the Scandinavian countries and Siberia. The farther south one goes the more these population fluctuations seem to level off. New Hampshire, for instance, is on the southern tier of areas which exhibit this phenomenon. In fact, even within the confines of our own state the periodic rise and fall of "cyclic" animals is most pronounced in Coos County, and least discernible along the Massachusetts line.

There are complications in the whole mystery. The "cycle" may reach a peak in one area one year while it may not hit a neighboring area until several years later. Various species of mice, lemmings, and voles seem to fluctuate in numbers approximately every four years, while that of hares, lynx and grouse seem to fall into a pattern of approximately ten years.

One of the star performers is the snowshoe hare. During peaks of abundance, such as in 1942, it was estimated that there were about 6,000 to the square mile in various sections of Canada. The following year they were very scarce and by 1944 one could drive a hundred miles without seeing a "rabbit".

Since the snowshoe hare goes to make up the main item of food for certain predators such as the lynx and snowy owl, the latter naturally build up in numbers when the hare becomes plentiful.

Then when the hare disappears, lynx and snowy owls find their food supply gone and within a year they also become very scarce. One follows the other in never ending population waves.

The big mystery about it all is the reason for these rises and declines. The Volume 18, No. 1 issue of the *Journal of Wildlife Management* devoted almost the entire issue to this complex subject. The concensus of the specialists seems to be that most clues point to nutrition deficiencies. Surely, this is obvious in the case of predators which must rely on prey species that fluctuate in numbers. It becomes less obvious, however, in the case of rodents and birds such as grouse. After these species build up in numbers to a saturation point Nature in some unknown manner then steps in, eradicates these animals by the millions, only to let the few survivors again build up another peak. Leopold, in his classic *Game Management,* makes some thought provoking statements in regard to the whole problem:

> "Cyclic phenomena are most strongly associated with northern animals . . . possessing specialized digestive capacity for living on low-grade foods (buds and bark) . . . Ability to live on low-grade food means immunity from winter starvation.
>
> Saturation phenomena (Leopold's term for population phenomena leading to 'flats', non-cyclic fluctuation in numbers), on the other hand, are most strongly associated with less specialized birds depending on seeds for winter survival, and hence not immune to winter starvation.
>
> The simplest inference is that the function of cycles is to hold within bounds those species which might otherwise, by reason of their immunity from starvation, increase to the point where they would devegetate their own ranges."

In its sheer magnitude this problem offers a challenge to science that has few peers in the realms of wildlife.

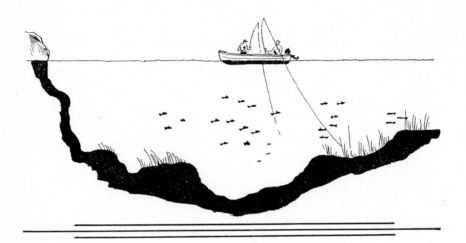

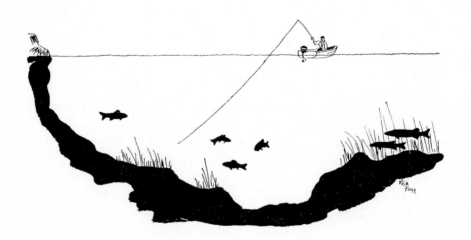

Carrying Capacity of Land and Water

One of the most important concepts to be remembered and understood in both fish and game work is that of "carrying capacity". Sportsmen, and even Fish and Game Departments, too often forget that a given piece of land or body of water can support and maintain from year to year only so many pounds of animal life.

Every farmer raising livestock thinks in terms of carrying capacity. He knows that his pasture will carry just so many head of cattle on an average year. If he attempts to hold more cows in this pasture than it can take care of, two things will happen: 1) his animals will become undernourished and 2) the pasture will be overgrazed so that in future years it will support still fewer cows.

Many people who accept this principle for growing livestock fail to recognize that it is equally applicable to fish in ponds, pheasants in fields, or deer in forests. But the fish and game manager must be constantly alert to avoid overstocking and to recognize the danger signals of overpopulations. When he examines the fish populations of a lake and finds that a large per cent of specimens are too small for their age, his first suspicion will be that there are too many fish for the carrying capacity of the lake. Fewer fish than it could hold would mean bigger and healthier fish.

Similarly, he will always be more concerned about finding too many deer in an area than too few, since he knows that the excess deer will reduce their own food supplies to the extent that in years to come that same range will have a lower carrying capacity for deer. On the other hand, a smaller number would have meant larger animals and these would have produced more fawns per year.

Thus fish and game populations should be kept slightly under the carrying capacity of their habitat rather than over, for this deficiency is relatively easy to correct. Overpopulations require much more drastic remedial measures and often the remedy takes many years to become effective.

Spring and Fall Turnover and Thermocline

A technical term gradually being used by more and more sportsmen is the word "thermocline". Not all who use the term are sure of what its precise meaning is, but they have a vague idea. They know it has something to do with lakes and they suspect that it somehow or other affects their fishing.

In early spring before the ice goes out, water in a lake just below the ice is just above 32° F., or very near to freezing. Deeper down in the lake the water will generally be slightly warmer, usually about 39° F. As any high school boy who has taken a course in physics knows, as water becomes colder it becomes more dense (and heavier) finally reaching its greatest density at approximately 39° F. Then as it gets colder and approaches freezing it begins to expand again, thus becoming lighter. Thus, the warmer and heavier water is at the bottom while the colder and lighter water is near the surface.

Then, as weather becomes warmer, the ice disappears and the surface water begins to warm up. Naturally, the water at the outer surface will warm up quicker than that somewhat lower, so it is first to reach a temperature of 39° F. Since it then is heavier than the water below, it begins to sink. This process continues (helped considerably by wind action) until the whole lake becomes the same temperature from top to bottom. Since it is now of the same density throughout, under the influence of spring winds it will circulate or mix from top to bottom. This is known as the "spring turnover". This situation may last several weeks. Of course, there are exceptions to the rule. Some lakes experience only partial turnovers.

Next we will see how the thermocline develops. But first, we wish to deny one assertion so often made by some New Hampshire natives. When ice turns "black" in spring and disappears, it does not sink to the bottom as ice, since ice is lighter than water.

The date of conclusion of this spring turnover varies from year to year depending on weather conditions. As it becomes warmer the temperature of the water on the surface of the lake rises. Every degree of heat added to the water makes it less dense and thereby lighter, consequently it loses its tendency to sink. As more and more of the water in the upper part of the lake warms up, the greater will it resist the action of the wind to make it circulate with colder water deeper down. Finally there comes a time when only the upper part of the lake circulates, since the colder water deeper down is too heavy.

About this time a strange phenomenon takes place. Many lakes, particularly the deeper ones, become divided into three sections: the uppermost warmer and circulating section which might be anywhere from about ten feet to approximately thirty feet in depth in New Hampshire lakes; the water at the bottom which remains cold, practically stationary, and has very little oxygen; and separating the upper from the lower there develops a narrow layer of water which is called the "thermocline". It is not clearly understood how this intermediate layer develops. How do we know where this layer is? We take temperature readings from top to bottom. At first the temperature drops gradually. When we come upon an area where the temperature drops at least one degree for every foot we go lower, that is the thermocline. Some of them show temperature drops as much as 4 degrees per foot of water. These layers vary in thickness, generally being much thicker in early summer than in late summer when lakes have become stabilized; at which time they may be anywhere from several to ten or fifteen feet in depth. The strange thing about this thermocline is that it seems to have the ability to keep the lower part of the lake separated from the upper part. Even the gases arising from the bottom gradually accumulate under the thermocline, since it does not permit them to break through to the top.

It has been pointed out that a thermocline can separate the upper portion of a lake from the lower portion so effectively that the two are entirely different chemically and from a temperature standpoint; also, that whereas water in the upper part circulates, it is practically stagnant in the lower section. Gases escaping from decaying organisms on the floor of the lake gradually build up underneath the thermocline, and oxygen is being steadily depleted until, soon, there is practically none left. Of course, there are exceptions where with some lakes having clean floors and bubbling springs this decrease of oxygen is not too serious.

How do thermoclines tie in with fish and fishing? It should be quite obvious that if oxygen disappears from a portion of a lake, fish will have to move out to avoid smothering to death. This they do by swimming up through the thermocline into the upper section where there is enough oxygen. But here fish are apt to run into temperature problems. In midsummer most lakes are too warm near the surface, particularly for trout. Consequently, as the weather becomes hotter these fish are gradually crowded nearer and nearer to the thermocline where water is coldest. Many fisherman take advantage of this, determining through the rise of a "maximum and minimum registering thermometer" how deep down the thermocline is, and then they fish just above it. Two biologists who are skin divers have told me that thermoclines even have a marked effect on plankton life. The upper section of a lake may be loaded with tiny organisms, very noticeable to the divers as they go down. When they reach the cold thermocline, however, plankton growth seems to end suddenly as if there were an invisible layer of cellophane keeping the organisms from sinking deeper down.

All of this changes in fall when the upper water begins to cool off, becomes heavier, and sinks. Gradually all the water in the lake is again in circulation and the period of fall turnover has arrived.

How To Call It

What to call the various members of the wildlife kingdom frequently results in controversy and even heated argument. In hopes it may help to settle some of these disputes, we hereby list some of the species and their proper designation.

SPECIES	MALE	FEMALE	YOUNG
Antelope	buck	doe	fawn
Bear	he-bear (boar)	she-bear (sow)	cub
Beaver	male	female	kit
Buffalo	bull	cow	calf
Caribou	buck	doe	fawn
Cats (large)	tom	lioness, etc.	cub
Cats (small)	tom	tabby	kitten
Coyotes	dog	bitch	whelp
Deer (white-tail, mule)	buck	doe	fawn
Duck	drake	duck	duckling
Elk	bull	cow	calf
Fox	dog fox	vixen	whelp (kit)
Goats	billy	nanny	kid
Goose	gander	goose	gosling
Moose	bull	cow	calf
Pheasant and Quail	cock	hen	chick
Rabbit	buck	doe	fawn
Sheep	ram	ewe	lamb
Swan	cob	pen	cygnet
Trout	buck (jack)	female	fry
Wolves	dog	bitch	whelp (cub, pup)

Vanishing Species

Most of us are quite aware of the fact that our ancestors and we have been part of a profligate, thoughtless, and shortsighted civilization. Nowhere has this been more vividly demonstrated than in the use and misuse of our natural resources. Mute testimony to this are the vanished and vanishing species of wildlife. Not all of us, however, realize how big this list has grown. We think of the passenger pigeon, and perhaps the heath hen, but do we know that the list has grown to the following extent?

Extinct or Threatened Wildlife

Great Auk
Carolina Paroquet
Labrador Duck
Gaudalupe Caracara
Heath Hen
Maine Giant Mink
California Grizzly Bear
Tejon Grizzly
Texas Grizzly
Plains Grizzly
Merriam Elk
Texas Mountain Sheep
Whooping Crane
Wolverine
Trumpeter Swan
Great White Heron
Eskimo Curlew
Masked Bobwhite
Everglades Kite
Gray Whale
Greenland Right Whale

Ivory Billed Woodpecker
Laysan Teal
Ipswich Sparrow
Sandhill Crane
Glacier Bear
Fisher
Blackfooted Ferret
Sea Otter
Desert Fox
Plains Fox
Guadalupe Fur Seal
Pacific Walrus
Atlantic Walrus
Eastern Fox Squirrel
Nelson Mountain Sheep
Sierra Mountain Sheep
Florida Manatee
Atlantic Right Whale
Passenger Pigeon
Kit Fox

The above list was compiled by the National Wildlife Federation.

301

Plant and Animal Publications in New Hampshire

Good books are a prime requisite for anyone planning to study the outdoors. Unfortunately, publications dealing specifically with the natural history of New Hampshire can practically be counted on the fingers of our two hands. We will try to list those we know about for the benefit of anyone planning to build up his reference library.

We believe that every library should contain Helenette Silver's *History of New Hampshire Game and Furbearers*, available from the Fish and Game Department and also numerous book stores for $2.85.

Like most other states, New Hampshire is no exception in having more publications dealing with birds than with the animal or plant groups. Although out of print, libraries will probably have the Proceedings of the Manchester Institute of Arts and Sciences, Vol. IV, 1902, which contains *The Birds of New Hampshire* by Allen. *The Birds of Durham and Vicinity* by Dearborn, 1903, *The Birds of the Lake Umbagog Region of Maine* by Brewster, *Birds at Concord, New Hampshire* by White, *Birds of Massachusetts and Other New England States* by Forbush, and *Birds between the Monadnocks* by Hill, should also be in various libraries of the State. Up-to-date checklists with distribution notes of birds in our States are *A List of the Birds of New Hampshire* by Richards, available from the Audubon Society at $1.00 per copy, and the small pocket-size list available from the Audubon Society or the N.H. Fish and Game Department at 5¢ a card.

Birds and Flowers about Concord, New Hampshire by Abbott, 1906, is listed in our State Library.

The Fishes of Eastern New Hampshire by Gordon, in New Hampshire Fish and Game Department's Biological Survey Report No. 2, *The Fishes of the Merrimack Watershed* by Bailey, in Biological Survey Report No. 3, and *The Fishes of the Connecticut Watershed* by Bailey and Oliver, in Biological Survey Report No. 4, are now out of print but can still be found in numerous libraries. *Fishes of New Hampshire* by Carpenter and

Siegler is still available at the N. H. Fish and Game Department office and various bookstores at 30¢ a copy.

All too little has been published dealing specifically with New Hampshire's mammals. *Blue Mountain Forest and its Animals* by Champollion, 1899, can be found in the State Library. *A List of New Hampshire Mammals and Their Distribution* by Carpenter and Siegler is still available at the New Hampshire Fish and Game Department. With the exception of numerous technical reports dealing with individual species, we know of no other literature.

Publications dealing with other animal groups are no less scarce. *Notes on the reptiles and amphibians of Intervale, New Hampshire* by Allen, 1879, appeared in the Boston Society of Natural History Proceedings, Vol. 29, No. 3. *Amphibians and Reptiles of New Hampshire* by Oliver and Bailey was published in the New Hampshire Fish and Game Department's Survey Report No. 4, and is now out of print. *Geographic Distribution of Snakes in New Hampshire* by Carle can be found in the 1951 Proceedings of the New Hampshire Academy of Science. In the same Proceedings is also a paper entitled *Nudibranchs of New Hampshire* by Moore. *Freshwater Shells of New Hampshire* by Clench and Russell, in the Fish and Game Department's Survey Report No. 3, and another paper with the same title and by the same authors, in Survey Report No. 4, are now both out of print.

Publications pertaining to New Hampshire's flora are also limited. *Plants of the Presidential Range* by Harris appeared in Vols. 23–27 of Appalachia. *Vascular Flora of Coos County* by Pease, 1926, may be found in various libraries. The very useful *Trees and Shrubs of New Hampshire* by Foster may be obtained from the Society for the Protection of New Hampshire Forests, for 35¢ a copy. *The Woody Plants of New Hampshire* by Hodgdon and Steele is available as Station Bull. 447 from the Agricultural Experiment Station, University of New Hampshire. *Ferns and Fern Allies of New Hampshire* by Scamman, can be obtained from the Secretary of the New Hampshire Academy of Science.

While there are undoubtedly others, they are not well known. New Hampshire needs more authors and more publishers who are willing to risk limited returns on a worthy venture.

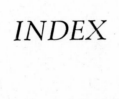

INDEX

Index

References are to pages of this volume.

315